Fractions in Action

Grades 3–6

Barbara Bando Irvin, Ph.D.

Table of Contents

Introduction

Fractions in Action utilizes three different types of fraction models to help students understand fraction concepts and operations with fractional numbers. The activities are designed for use with your mathematics curriculum for grades 3 through 6.

This activity book contains three major sections focusing on basic fraction concepts. The sections utilize three fraction models:

- Rainbow Fraction Circles
- Rainbow Fraction Squares
- Rainbow Fraction Tiles

Each section focuses on the following skills:

- Equivalent fractions
- Comparing fractions
- Adding and subtracting fractions
- Multiplying and dividing fractions

Each section also contains activities to connect fraction concepts to other mathematical topics such as:

- Circle graphs
- Decimals
- Percent
- Number lines
- Measurement
- Central angle measurement
- Clocks
- 24-Hour Day

Feel free to use a particular fraction model to develop a concept or demonstrate a concept that correlates to a textbook lesson or curriculum objective.

You may wish to use several different fraction models at a time to explore a particular concept. For example, to compare fractions, you may wish to use the fraction circles one day and the fraction squares another day. Or you may use one fraction model at a time to help students develop an understanding of several fraction concepts.

Although all three fraction models deal with the same concepts and skills, it is necessary for students to get a different visual perspective of fractional parts and how they are named, compared, and operated upon. This exposure helps them to generalize and transfer their knowledge about fractions.

Using This Book

This book contains more than 60 blackline master activities using fraction models to help students understand fraction concepts and operations with fractional numbers. In addition to the reproducible blackline masters, *Teaching Notes* at the beginning of each section give an overview of the fraction model and a selection of basic fraction activities.

Objectives are included to help correlate the activities with your textbook or mathematics curriculum guide. Specific teaching suggestions are provided under the titles *Warm Up, Using the Activity Pages,* and *Wrap Up.*

In the section *Solutions,* pages 92–95, you will find answers to all of the problems. Use the **Wonderful Work Certificate** and the **Fractions Are Easy Award** on the last page to praise students on their improved work habits, social skills, and academic accomplishments.

To ensure a successful classroom demonstration and student activity, practice the activity yourself with the fraction models. Demonstrate the fraction activities on the overhead projector. Many of the activity blackline masters may be used as overhead transparency masters.

Have students work on their blackline masters as you demonstrate the same blackline master on the overhead. Urge students to model the activities shown on the blackline master pages. Have them record their responses by drawing pictures of the hands-on experience, working out the problems, and writing explanations of their work.

Students can work individually, in pairs, or in cooperative small groups. Use the activities as part of a specific mathematics lesson, or in a learning center where students can work independently. Since some of the activities require more than one set of fraction models, two or three students may have to work together.

Encourage students to share their discoveries and solutions with their classmates. Suggest that students write about their ideas by making a storybook, writing in a journal, or creating their own problems and puzzles to challenge each other.

NCTM Standards

Curriculum and Evaluation Standards for School Mathematics, published by the National Council of Teachers of Mathematics (NCTM), was used as a guide in writing this book. Special attention was given to standards 5, 6, 7, and 12. Standard 12 focuses on fractional numbers for grades K–4. Standards 5, 6, and 7 focus on number relationships and computation. These standards suggest that the mathematics curriculum dealing with fractions should include these goals for students:

- Understand and appreciate the need for fractional numbers.
- Develop concepts of fractions and mixed numbers.
- Develop number sense for fractional numbers.
- Develop and use order relationships for fractions.
- Use models to find equivalent fractions.
- Use models to explore operations on fractions.
- Compute with whole numbers and fractions.
- Apply fractions to problem situations.
- Use models to investigate relationships among fractions, decimals, and percents.

Rainbow Fraction Models

Each set of Deluxe Rainbow Fraction models includes ones, halves, thirds, fourths, fifths, sixths, eighths, tenths, and twelfths. The classroom and overhead sets are listed below.

Rainbow Fraction Circle Models
  LER 617 *Deluxe Rainbow Fraction Circles*
  LER 618 *Overhead Deluxe Rainbow Fraction Circles*
Rainbow Fraction Square Models
  LER 619 *Deluxe Rainbow Fraction Squares*
  LER 620 *Overhead Deluxe Rainbow Fraction Squares*
Rainbow Fraction Tile Models
  LER 615 *Rainbow Fraction Tiles*
  LER 616 *Overhead Rainbow Fraction Tiles*

Blackline masters are provided for all fraction models within each section of activities. Have students color and cut out their own sets of fraction models. Make two or even three sets of each fraction model and five or six cutouts of the "1" piece so they can deal with improper fractions, mixed numbers, unit fractions, and proper fractions. Provide large envelopes or resealable plastic bags for students to store their fraction model sets.

Fraction Names, Colors, and Symbols

All the sets of Deluxe Rainbow Fraction models are color coded the same way for consistency. This consistency enables students to make connections among fractional parts even though they have different unit-fraction shapes.

Deluxe Rainbow Fraction Models

one	red	1
halves	pink	$\frac{1}{2}, \frac{2}{2}$
thirds	orange	$\frac{1}{3}, \frac{2}{3}, \frac{3}{3}$
fourths	yellow	$\frac{1}{4}, \frac{2}{4}, \frac{3}{4}, \frac{4}{4}$
fifths	green	$\frac{1}{5}, \frac{2}{5}, \frac{3}{5}, \frac{4}{5}, \frac{5}{5}$
sixths	teal	$\frac{1}{6}, \frac{2}{6}, \frac{3}{6}, \frac{4}{6}, \frac{5}{6}, \frac{6}{6}$
eighths	blue	$\frac{1}{8}, \frac{2}{8}, \frac{3}{8}, \frac{4}{8}, \frac{5}{8}, \frac{6}{8}, \frac{7}{8}, \frac{8}{8}$
tenths	purple	$\frac{1}{10}, \frac{2}{10}, \frac{3}{10}, \frac{4}{10}, \frac{5}{10}, \frac{6}{10}, \frac{7}{10}, \frac{8}{10}, \frac{9}{10}, \frac{10}{10}$
twelfths	black	$\frac{1}{12}, \frac{2}{12}, \frac{3}{12}, \frac{4}{12}, \frac{5}{12}, \frac{6}{12}, \frac{7}{12}, \frac{8}{12}, \frac{9}{12}, \frac{10}{12}, \frac{11}{12}, \frac{12}{12}$

Fraction Vocabulary

As students work with the fraction models, they should become familiar with the following vocabulary:

numerator	*greater than*
denominator	*less than*
fraction	*lowest terms*
improper fraction	*part/whole*
proper fraction	*compare*
unit fraction	*"trade"*
mixed number	*add*
common denominator	*subtract*
unlike denominator	*multiply*
equivalent	*divide*

It is important that students communicate their ideas along with the use of

Fractions in Action
© 1994 Learning Resources, Inc.

Rainbow Fraction Circles
Teaching Notes

Objectives

Use Deluxe Rainbow Fraction Circles:

- To model equivalent fractions and to compare fractions.
- To perform operations using fractions, whole numbers, and mixed numbers.
- To relate fractions to analog clock time, percent, degrees, and circle graphs.

 ## Warm Up

Initiate a discussion about how a large round cookie, a pie, a round cake, a cheese wheel, or a pizza might be divided evenly among a pair or a small group of students. Have students draw and color a picture of a large round pizza, cookie, pie, or cake on a large paper plate. Ask students to compare the fractional parts. Challenge students to divide their paper-plate pictures into equal-sized parts so that everyone in the class will get a slice.

Students should discover these two tenets about unit fractions: (1) The paper plate must be divided equally among themselves to get a "fair share," and (2) The larger the group, the smaller each slice is for each of them.

Observe students to see if they can identify the fractional parts of a fraction circle before they start doing the activities on pages 15 through 46.

Fraction Circle Materials

Deluxe Rainbow Fraction Circles (LER 617)

Deluxe Overhead Rainbow Fraction Circles (LER 618)

Blackline masters on pages 12, 13, 14

 ## Using the Activity Pages

Naming Fractions *(page 15)*

Use this activity page as an overhead transparency master to display various unit and proper fractions and to show how they are labeled. Distribute copies of this page to the students to follow along. Demonstrate that *equal-sized* pieces are needed to show a unit or proper fraction having a particular denominator. Emphasize the vocabulary words *numerator* and *denominator*.

Names for 1 *(page 16)*

Using this page, students are to discover that another name for 1 is $\frac{n}{n}$ (i.e., $1 = \frac{2}{2}$ or $1 = \frac{5}{5}$). The last exercise helps students extend their thinking to include fractions constructed from the fraction circle pieces. Students could show that 16 sixteenths equals 1 by making a fraction circle model for $\frac{1}{8}$s and then halving each $\frac{1}{8}$ piece to make $\frac{1}{16}$ pieces.

Equivalent Fractions (*pages 17–18*)

The three exercises on page 17 encourage students to try all the different colors (sizes) of fraction pieces to find fractions equivalent to $\frac{1}{2}$, $\frac{1}{3}$, and $\frac{1}{4}$. In the exercise for $\frac{1}{2}$, it is obvious that the $\frac{1}{2}$ piece (pink) will cover the drawing on the page exactly. The $\frac{\square}{2}$ should be filled in to show "$\frac{1}{2}$".

However, the $\frac{1}{3}$ piece (orange) or even two $\frac{1}{3}$ pieces do not cover the drawing exactly. The $\frac{\square}{3}$ should be crossed out because there aren't any number of thirds that will cover $\frac{1}{2}$ exactly.

Using $\frac{1}{4}$ pieces (yellow), students should discover that two fourths are equivalent to $\frac{1}{2}$. Then they should fill in the $\frac{\square}{4}$ to show "$\frac{2}{4}$" and draw a ring around it.

Page 18 is a summary of pages 16 and 17 and may be used as a reference sheet for those who have difficulty remembering equivalent fractions for 1, $\frac{1}{2}$, and $\frac{1}{3}$.

Lowest-terms Equivalent Fractions (*page 19*)

Have students draw a picture of the fraction pieces used. Fill in the fraction boxes for each lowest-terms fraction. They should discover that the lowest-terms fraction uses the least number of same-color fraction pieces.

Naming & Comparing Fractions (*pages 20–23*)

Pages 20 and 21 are used to show the size of the Rainbow Fraction Circles set. On page 20, students see how one unit fraction compares with another unit fraction. At the bottom of the page, students create a "rainbow" of sizes by starting with the $\frac{1}{2}$ piece. They then put the $\frac{1}{3}$ piece on top of $\frac{1}{2}$ to see $\frac{1}{3}$ is smaller than $\frac{1}{2}$, and then put the $\frac{1}{4}$ piece on top to

see that $\frac{1}{4}$ is smaller than $\frac{1}{3}$ and smaller than $\frac{1}{2}$. The first two exercises on page 21 present a summary of the "rainbow" activity begun on page 20.

On page 22, students find all the fraction circle fractions that are larger than $\frac{2}{3}$ and all the fractions that are less than $\frac{1}{2}$. If students find more fractions than the number of fraction box figures given, tell them to express their fractions in lowest terms. Using this page as a transparency, demonstrate fraction pieces that "cover" the figures for $\frac{2}{3}$ and $\frac{1}{2}$ to find the solutions. By doing these exercises, students can get a feel for finding fractions greater than or less than a given fraction.

The two unit circles on page 23 are provided as a workspace. Students show which fraction is larger or smaller by showing one fraction alongside the other. If the pair of fractions seems quite close in size, have the students move the pieces of one fraction on top of the other fraction. For example, $\frac{7}{10}$ and $\frac{2}{3}$ may look quite similar. Move the two $\frac{1}{3}$s to cover the $\frac{7}{10}$ on the other circle to see that $\frac{2}{3}$ does not quite cover $\frac{7}{10}$ completely; therefore, $\frac{2}{3} < \frac{7}{10}$.

Improper Fractions to Mixed Numbers (*page 24*)

Students will need at least two sets of Rainbow Fraction Circles for this activity. The two unit circles are provided as a workspace. Students express an improper fraction as a mixed number by writing the mixed number and drawing a picture of it. Students should draw their pictures using all unit fraction pieces. For example, $\frac{5}{4}$ can be shown as $\frac{4}{4}$ on the first circle and $\frac{1}{4}$ on the second circle.

Adding Fractions *(pages 25–31)*

These activities show students how to add fractions using the Rainbow Fraction Circles. In order for you and the students to know that the correct answer has been found, students are to draw a picture of the sum and write the fraction or mixed number. The picture should show the fraction pieces used. The following skills are presented:

Page 25: Adding fractions with common denominators, find lowest-terms sum.

Page 26: Adding fractions with common denominators, find lowest-terms mixed number sums.

Page 27: Finding a common denominator for two fractions with unlike denominators.

Page 28: Adding fractions with unlike denominators.

Page 29: Adding fractions with unlike denominators, find lowest-terms sum.

Page 30: Adding fractions with unlike denominators, find lowest-terms mixed number sum.

Page 31: Finding missing addends to make sums of 1.

Subtracting Fractions *(pages 32–35)*

After students have figured out how to add fractions using the fraction circles, subtracting with the fraction circle models is quite similar. They "take away" fraction pieces from the larger fractional number to find the difference. Pictorial examples showing subtraction with fraction circle pieces are shown at the top of each page. The following skills are presented on pages 32–35:

Page 32: Subtracting fractions with common denominators, find lowest-terms difference.

Page 33: Subtracting fractions with unlike denominators, find lowest-terms difference.

Page 34: Subtracting fractions from mixed numbers, find lowest-terms difference.

Page 35: Subtracting fractions from mixed or whole numbers, find lowest-terms difference.

The problems on page 35 present an added challenge. The mixed numbers or whole numbers must not only be expressed using common denominators, but must also be regrouped to an improper fraction in order to subtract one number from the other.

For $1\frac{1}{4} - \frac{1}{2}$, students first express the fractions with a common denominator, $1\frac{1}{4} - \frac{2}{4}$. Then express $1\frac{1}{4}$ as $\frac{5}{4}$ so that $\frac{2}{4}$ can be subtracted. Students will need at least two sets of fraction circles to complete the exercises on pages 34 and 35.

Multiplying Fractions *(pages 36–38)*

Two multiplication examples are presented using the fraction circles—a whole number times a fraction and a unit fraction times a fraction. Multiplying fractions and mixed numbers by each other is shown using shaded figures on grid paper or other methods.

On pages 36 and 37, multiplying a fraction by a whole number is most closely associated with multiplication using whole numbers in that students can refer to repeated addition. For $3 \times \frac{5}{8}$, there are 3 groups of $\frac{5}{8}$ or $\frac{5}{8} + \frac{5}{8} + \frac{5}{8} = \frac{15}{8} = 1\frac{7}{8}$. Urge students to express the product for the last three problems in lowest terms.

On page 38, students think of a fractional part of a fraction, which is difficult to do. Work several examples with the students, having them trace a fraction on a piece of paper and then finding a fractional part of it. For $\frac{1}{2}$ of $\frac{3}{4}$, represent $\frac{3}{4}$ with the fraction circle pieces and then trace around them on a piece of paper. Cut out the figure showing $\frac{3}{4}$ and then fold it in half. Now try to cover half of $\frac{3}{4}$ with the other fraction circle pieces. Three $\frac{1}{8}$ fraction circle pieces should cover $\frac{1}{2}$ of $\frac{3}{4}$

exactly to show that $\frac{1}{2}$ of $\frac{3}{4} = \frac{3}{8}$. Challenge students to express the products for the last two problems in lowest terms.

Dividing Fractions *(pages 39–40)*

When dividing with fractions, the basic concept of division should be emphasized: "How many ___ are contained in ___?" or "How many ___ can cover ___?" You may wish to present some pattern problems to help students grasp the meaning of division. For example, ask:
How many $\frac{1}{4}$s are there in 1? *[4]* which is similar to: How many quarters in $1? *[4]*
How many $\frac{1}{4}$s are there in 3? *[12]*

When working with fractions, students will be confused to find that dividing fractions by fractions may yield a quotient larger than either fraction in the division problem. Why does $\frac{1}{2} \div \frac{1}{6} = 3$? It takes three $\frac{1}{6}$ pieces to cover $\frac{1}{2}$ exactly. In other words, $\frac{1}{6}$ fits into $\frac{1}{2}$ three times.

Ask students to estimate whether the answer to a fraction division problem will be more than or less than 1. To grasp this concept, ask whether the divisor is larger or smaller than the dividend.

Sometimes it is better to work with unlabeled fraction models. The answer is not necessarily what it says on the fraction piece, but how it is related to the dividend.

On pages 39 and 40, remind students to think how many times the divisor will cover the dividend when using the fraction circle models.

Another method when dividing with fractions is changing to common denominators.
How many $\frac{1}{4}$s in 1? means: "How many $\frac{1}{4}$s in $\frac{4}{4}$ or $\frac{4}{4} \div \frac{1}{4}$"? *[4]*
How many $\frac{1}{4}$s in 3? means: "How many $\frac{1}{4}$s in $\frac{12}{4}$ or $\frac{12}{4} \div \frac{1}{4}$"? *[12]*

Fraction Connection to Time
(pages 41–42)

Warm Up: Direct the students to look at the clock or at their watches. Ask them to name a fraction that tells how far around the clock face the minute hand moved from 10:00 to 10:30 [$\frac{1}{2}$ *for 30 minutes*] or from 10:30 to 10:45 [$\frac{1}{4}$ *for 15 minutes*] or from 10:45 to 10:50 [$\frac{1}{12}$ *for 5 minutes*].

Have the students complete the exercises on page 41 by placing various fraction circle pieces on the clock face. Discuss the solutions relating to multiplication of a fraction and a whole number; i.e., $\frac{1}{3}$ of 60 minutes is 20 minutes or $\frac{1}{3} \times 60 = 20$.

Before assigning the exercises on page 42, ascertain that students know what a circle graph is and how it is interpreted. You may wish to have students talk about a school day or a Saturday or Sunday over a 12-hour period. For these two exercises, they soon will discover that the $\frac{1}{12}$ piece represents one hour. Challenge some students to make a graph of their activities using a 24-hour day circle graph, which they will encounter later on page 46.

Fraction Connection to Degrees
(page 43)

Warm Up: Initiate a discussion about rotation and how many degrees there are in a complete revolution [*360°*]. Tell students that angles are measured in degrees and with a *protractor*. This protractor shows 360°. Most protractors are semicircles and only show 180°.

In order to find a fractional part of a complete revolution, have students place a fraction circle piece on the protractor aligning one straight edge of the piece with 0 (or along the "cut" line shown). Relate each exercise to multiplication of fractions and whole numbers; i.e., $\frac{1}{8}$ of 360° is 45°. Ask students to find $\frac{3}{8}$ of a complete revolution if they know how many degrees are represented by $\frac{1}{8}$. Inform the students they are finding the *central angle* of this circle.

Have the students make a Degree Wheel. This device will help them figure out the central angle measurements for the circle graph problems on pages 45 and 46.

Fraction Connection to Percent
(page 44)

Warm Up: Since there are 100 cents in a dollar, relate percent to a "cent" circle. Have students make a paper-plate silver dollar. Assign several students to cut the "silver dollar" into 2 pieces ($\frac{1}{2}$, *half dollar, 50 cents*), 4 pieces ($\frac{1}{4}$, *quarter, 25 cents*), 10 pieces ($\frac{1}{10}$, *dime, 10 cents*), 20 pieces ($\frac{1}{20}$, *nickel, 5 cents*), and, if some students can do it, also 100 pieces ($\frac{1}{100}$, *penny, 1 cent*). Ask students to find money equivalents using these silver dollar pieces; i.e., $\frac{1}{2} = \frac{5}{10}$. Inform students that *percent* means "per hundred." Show that a dime or $\frac{1}{10}$ of a dollar is also 10%. Some students may also connect this activity to decimals.

On page 44, have students place a fraction circle piece on the percent circle aligning one straight edge of the piece with 0 (or along the "cut" line shown). Relate each exercise to multiplication of fractions and whole numbers; i.e., $\frac{1}{8}$ of 100 is $12\frac{1}{2}$%.

Have students make a Percent Wheel and compare their answers at the top of the page. Remind students this device will help them figure the central angle measurements for the circle graph problems on pages 45 and 46.

Fraction Connection to Circle Graphs *(pages 45–46)*

Warm Up: Have a "Show and Tell" about circle graphs. Ask students to find circle

graphs in newspapers, magazines, or their textbooks. Ask them to interpret the labels and the sections on their graphs and explain why a circle graph was used rather than using a bar or a line-segment graph.

On page 45, students are asked to interpret two circle graphs. Page 46 is more difficult in that the students are to construct circle graphs. Encourage students to use the Degree and Percent Wheels and Rainbow Fraction Circle pieces in order to complete pages 45 and 46. Although the complete circle graphs on page 46 may appear different (due to the placement of the sections), the size of the sections should be the same. These two pages present an opportunity for students to work together in small cooperative groups, especially to figure out the central angles on page 46.

Wrap Up

Performance evaluation. Ask students to use the Rainbow Fraction Circles to identify a fraction and to find equivalent fractions. Using very simple problem situations, ask students to add or subtract fractions using the fraction circles to ascertain that they understand the concept.

Written assessment. Working in pairs or small cooperative groups, have the students select a project to show how to find equivalent fractions.

Fraction Circles

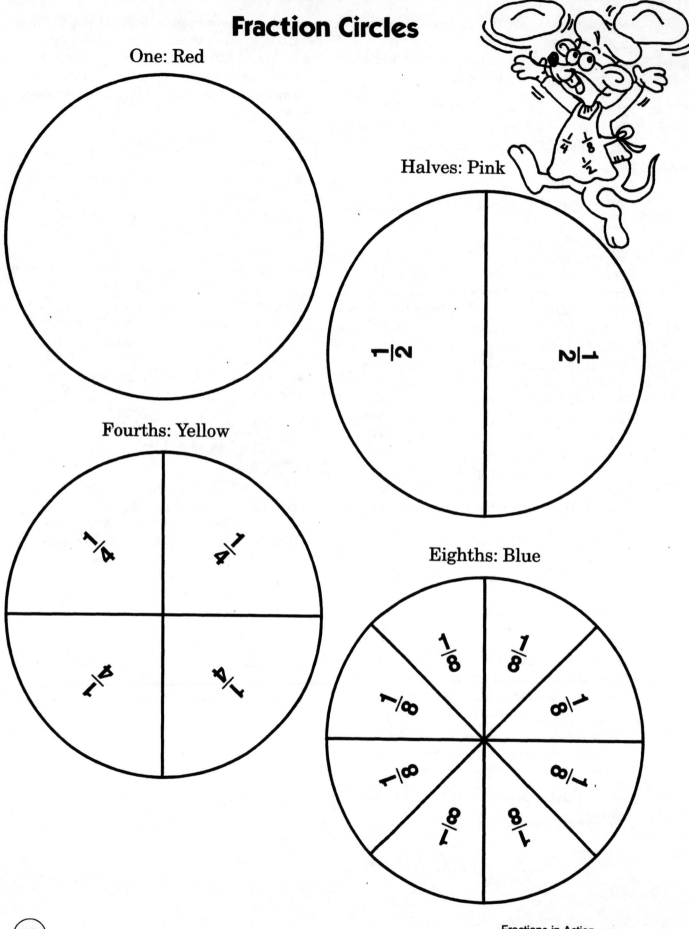

One: Red

Halves: Pink

$\frac{1}{2}$ $\frac{1}{2}$

Fourths: Yellow

$\frac{1}{4}$ $\frac{1}{4}$ $\frac{1}{4}$ $\frac{1}{4}$

Eighths: Blue

$\frac{1}{8}$ $\frac{1}{8}$ $\frac{1}{8}$ $\frac{1}{8}$ $\frac{1}{8}$ $\frac{1}{8}$ $\frac{1}{8}$ $\frac{1}{8}$

Fractions in Action
© 1994 Learning Resources, Inc.

Fraction Circles

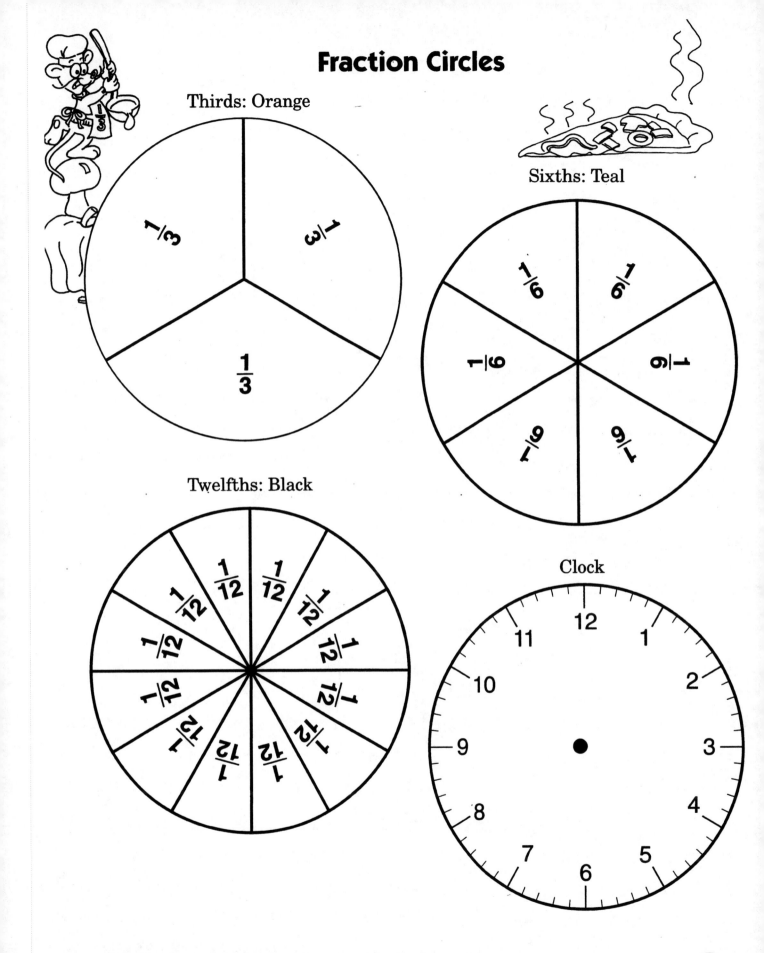

Thirds: Orange

$\frac{1}{3}$ $\frac{1}{3}$ $\frac{1}{3}$

Sixths: Teal

$\frac{1}{6}$ $\frac{1}{6}$ $\frac{1}{6}$ $\frac{1}{6}$ $\frac{1}{6}$ $\frac{1}{6}$

Twelfths: Black

$\frac{1}{12}$ $\frac{1}{12}$ $\frac{1}{12}$ $\frac{1}{12}$ $\frac{1}{12}$ $\frac{1}{12}$ $\frac{1}{12}$ $\frac{1}{12}$ $\frac{1}{12}$ $\frac{1}{12}$ $\frac{1}{12}$ $\frac{1}{12}$

Clock

11 12 1
10   2
9   3
8   4
7   6   5

Fraction Circles

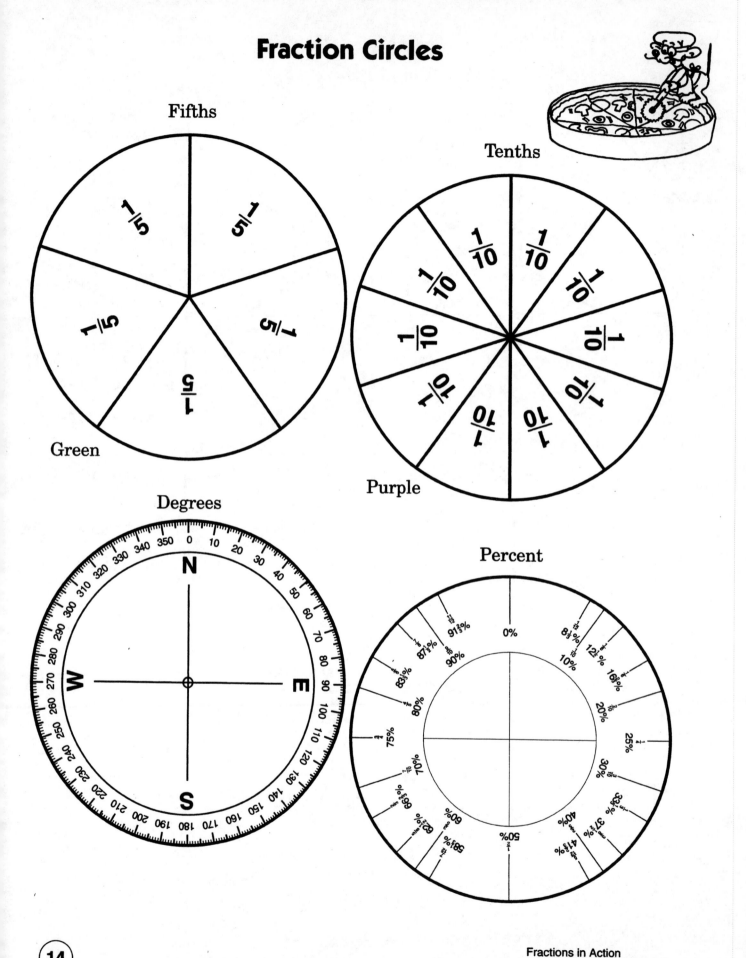

Fifths

Green

Tenths

Purple

Degrees

Percent

Fractions in Action
© 1994 Learning Resources, Inc.

Name That Fraction

Name_____

➤ Look at the fraction circle. Choose a color and place all
the pieces of that same color on the circle.

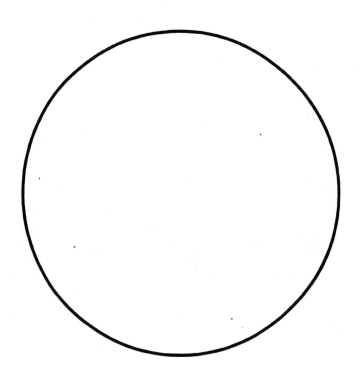

What is the color? _____

How many pieces fit
exactly on the circle? _____

Each piece is:
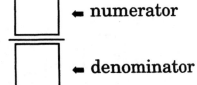
⟵ numerator

⟵ denominator

One-Color Cover

Name _____

➤ Use your fraction circles to find how many same-color pieces cover the unit circle exactly.

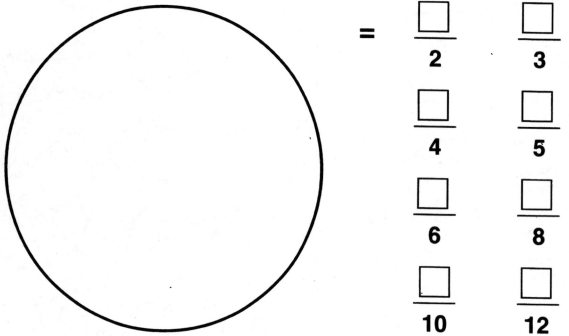

$= \dfrac{\square}{2} \qquad \dfrac{\square}{3}$

$\dfrac{\square}{4} \qquad \dfrac{\square}{5}$

$\dfrac{\square}{6} \qquad \dfrac{\square}{8}$

$\dfrac{\square}{10} \qquad \dfrac{\square}{12}$

➤ Use the information you gathered to find the fractions equivalent to 1. Fill in the fraction boxes.

$$1 = \frac{2}{2} = \frac{\square}{3} = \frac{4}{\square} = \frac{\square}{\square} = \frac{\square}{\square} = \frac{8}{\square} = \frac{\square}{10} = \frac{\square}{\square}$$

➤ Did you notice a pattern above? Can you fill in the numerators?

$$1 = \frac{\square}{9} = \frac{\square}{15} = \frac{\square}{16} = \frac{\square}{20} = \frac{\square}{24} = \frac{\square}{25} = \frac{\square}{50} = \frac{\square}{100}$$

Cover-Up

Name_____

➤ Find same-color fraction circles that will cover each figure below exactly. Fill in the fraction boxes for the fractions that show which pieces cover the figure exactly. Circle the equivalent fractions.

➤ Cross out the fractions that are not equivalent to the figure shown.

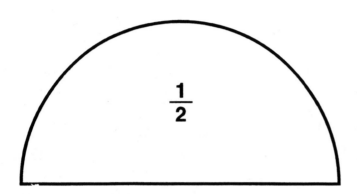

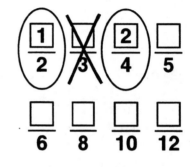

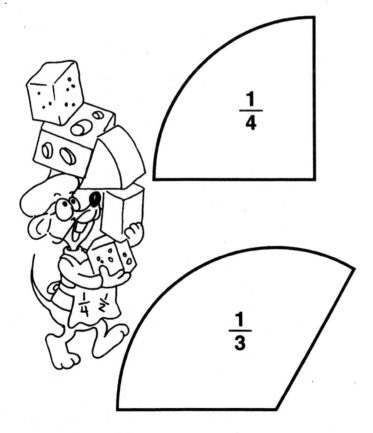

Same but Different

Name_____

➤ Use your fraction circles to find equivalent fractions for each figure below.

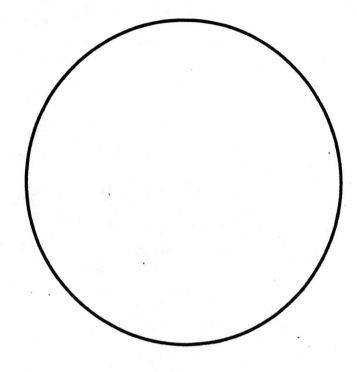

$$1 = \frac{\square}{\square} = \frac{\square}{\square} = \frac{\square}{\square}$$

$$= \frac{\square}{\square} = \frac{\square}{\square} = \frac{\square}{\square}$$

$$= \frac{\square}{\square} = \frac{\square}{\square}$$

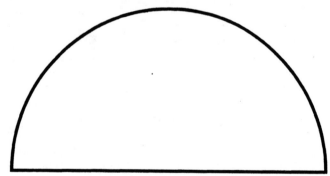

$$\frac{1}{2} = \frac{\square}{\square} = \frac{\square}{\square} = \frac{\square}{\square}$$

$$= \frac{\square}{\square} = \frac{\square}{\square}$$

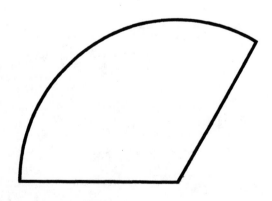

$$\frac{1}{3} = \frac{\square}{\square} = \frac{\square}{\square}$$

Fractions in Action
© 1994 Learning Resources, Inc.

How Low Can You Go?

Name_____

➤ Make each fraction using your fraction circles. Show an equivalent fraction with as few fraction circles as you can.

➤ Draw a picture of the lowest-terms fraction in the circle at the right, and write the fraction under it.

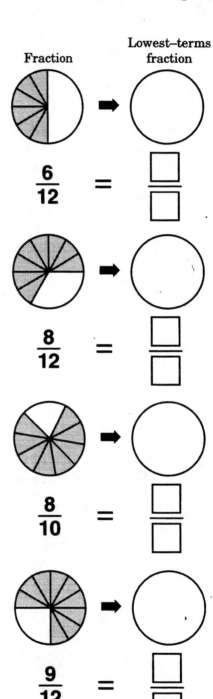

	Fraction		Lowest-terms fraction

$$\frac{4}{8} = \frac{1}{2}$$

$$\frac{4}{6} = \frac{\square}{\square}$$

$$\frac{5}{10} = \frac{\square}{\square}$$

$$\frac{4}{12} = \frac{\square}{\square}$$

$$\frac{6}{12} = \frac{\square}{\square}$$

$$\frac{8}{12} = \frac{\square}{\square}$$

$$\frac{8}{10} = \frac{\square}{\square}$$

$$\frac{9}{12} = \frac{\square}{\square}$$

Make a Rainbow

➤ Cover each figure with a fraction circle. Label the figure.

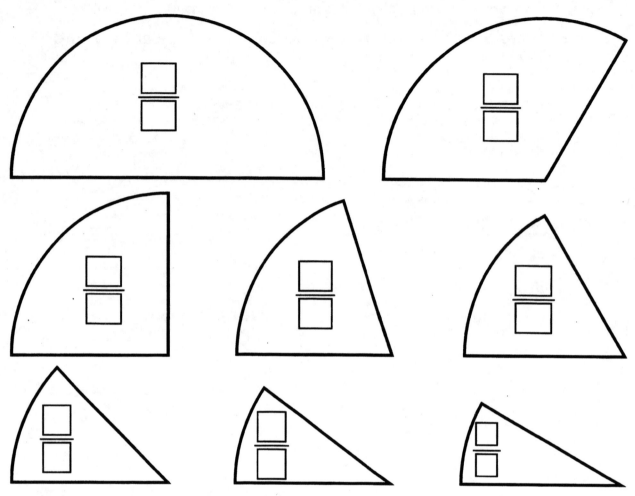

➤ Make a "rainbow." Start with the $\frac{1}{2}$ piece, then the next smallest piece, until you have a pink to black rainbow. Fill in the fraction boxes.

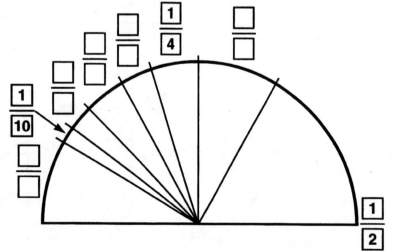

Fractions in Action
© 1994 Learning Resources, Inc.

Rainbow Revisited

Name_____

➤ Use your fraction circles to make a "rainbow" on the unit circle.

➤ Fill in the boxes with unit fractions around the circle.

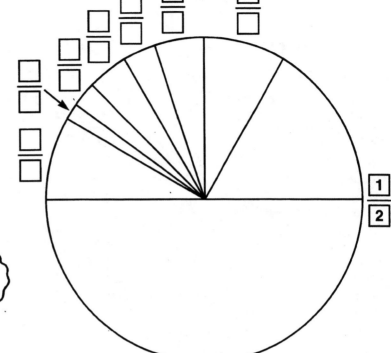

➤ Fill in the fraction boxes to show the order of fractions from smallest to largest.

$$\frac{1}{12} < \frac{1}{10} < \frac{\Box}{\Box} < \frac{\Box}{\Box} < \frac{\Box}{\Box} < \frac{\Box}{\Box} < \frac{\Box}{\Box} < \frac{1}{2}$$

➤ Fill in the fraction boxes to show the order of fractions from largest to smallest.

$$\frac{1}{2} > \frac{\Box}{\Box} > \frac{1}{4} > \frac{\Box}{\Box} > \frac{\Box}{\Box} > \frac{\Box}{\Box} > \frac{\Box}{\Box} > \frac{1}{12}$$

➤ Use <, =, or > to show the relationship between each pair of fractions.

$\frac{1}{6} \bigcirc \frac{1}{3}$ $\frac{1}{2} \bigcirc \frac{1}{4}$ $\frac{1}{8} \bigcirc \frac{1}{4}$ $\frac{1}{5} \bigcirc \frac{1}{4}$

$\frac{1}{3} \bigcirc \frac{1}{12}$ $\frac{1}{10} \bigcirc \frac{1}{12}$ $\frac{1}{2} \bigcirc \frac{1}{6}$ $\frac{1}{8} \bigcirc \frac{1}{10}$

Less Than, Greater Than

Name _____

➤ Use your fraction circles to find lowest-terms fractions that are larger than $\frac{2}{3}$ but less than 1.

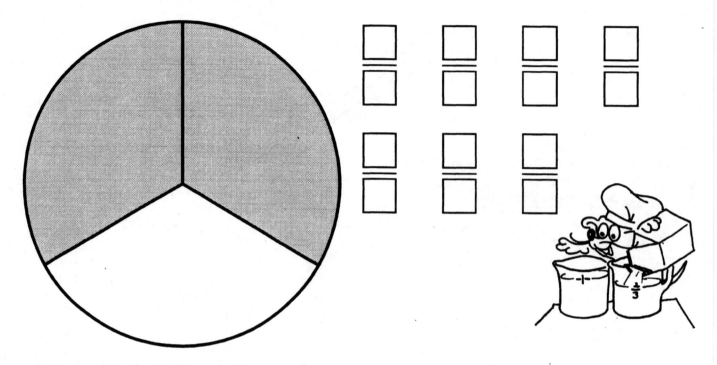

➤ Use your fraction circles to find lowest-terms fractions that are less than $\frac{1}{2}$ but greater than 0.

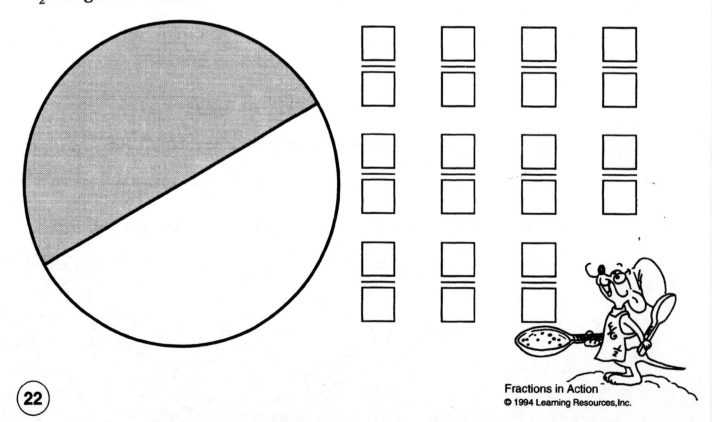

Fractions in Action
© 1994 Learning Resources, Inc.

Compare the Pairs

Name_____

➤ Place your fraction circles on the unit circles here
the pairs of fractions below. Use <, =, or > to show
relationship between the fractions.

$\dfrac{1}{2} \bigcirc \dfrac{3}{6}$ $\dfrac{1}{3} \bigcirc \dfrac{2}{12}$ $\dfrac{1}{4} \bigcirc \dfrac{2}{5}$ $\dfrac{1}{6} \bigcirc \dfrac{2}{3}$

$\dfrac{2}{5} \bigcirc \dfrac{3}{10}$ $\dfrac{4}{6} \bigcirc \dfrac{2}{3}$ $\dfrac{7}{10} \bigcirc \dfrac{6}{8}$ $\dfrac{4}{5} \bigcirc \dfrac{3}{4}$

$\dfrac{4}{12} \bigcirc \dfrac{2}{6}$ $\dfrac{2}{8} \bigcirc \dfrac{3}{12}$ $\dfrac{7}{8} \bigcirc \dfrac{7}{12}$ $\dfrac{1}{3} \bigcirc \dfrac{3}{8}$

Find the Mixed Number

Name_____

➤ Use two sets of fraction circles to show fractions greater than 1.

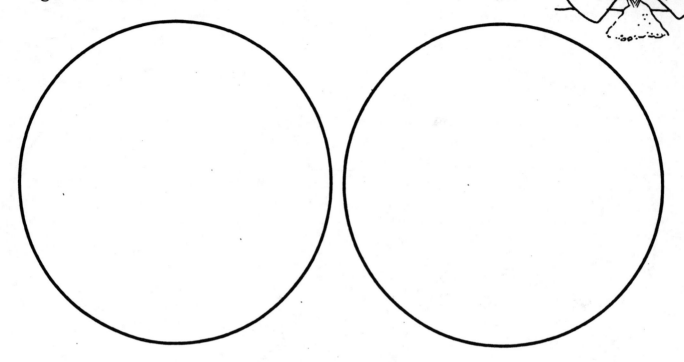

➤ Find the mixed number and draw a fraction picture on the circles to show your work.

Mixed number	Fraction picture		Mixed number	Fraction picture		Mixed number	Fraction picture

$\frac{4}{3}$ = ___ ◯ ◯ $\frac{8}{5}$ = ___ ◯ ◯ $\frac{7}{4}$ = ___ ◯ ◯

$\frac{7}{6}$ = ___ ◯ ◯ $\frac{13}{8}$ = ___ ◯ ◯ $\frac{19}{12}$ = ___ ◯ ◯

➤ For each improper fraction, write the lowest-terms mixed number and draw a picture of it.

Lowest-terms mixed number	Fraction picture		Lowest-terms mixed number	Fraction picture		Lowest-terms mixed number	Fraction picture

$\frac{6}{4}$ = ___ ◯ ◯ $\frac{10}{8}$ = ___ ◯ ◯ $\frac{9}{6}$ = ___ ◯ ◯

$\frac{12}{10}$ = ___ ◯ ◯ $\frac{15}{12}$ = ___ ◯ ◯ $\frac{10}{6}$ = ___ ◯ ◯

Adding Fractions: Common Denominators

Name_____

➤ Use your fraction circles to find each sum.

➤ Draw a picture of the sum to show your work.

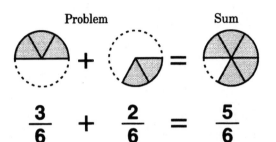

$$\frac{3}{6} + \frac{2}{6} = \frac{5}{6}$$

Problem	Sum	Fraction picture

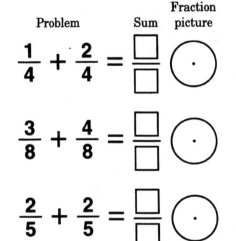

$$\frac{1}{4} + \frac{2}{4} = \frac{\square}{\square} \bigcirc$$

$$\frac{3}{8} + \frac{4}{8} = \frac{\square}{\square} \bigcirc$$

$$\frac{2}{5} + \frac{2}{5} = \frac{\square}{\square} \bigcirc$$

$$\frac{1}{6} + \frac{4}{6} = \frac{\square}{\square} \bigcirc$$

$$\frac{3}{10} + \frac{4}{10} = \frac{\square}{\square} \bigcirc$$

$$\frac{5}{12} + \frac{2}{12} = \frac{\square}{\square} \bigcirc$$

➤ Express each sum as a lowest-terms fraction.

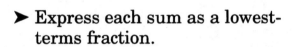

$$\frac{2}{6} + \frac{1}{6} = \frac{3}{6} = \frac{1}{2}$$

Problem	Sum	Lowest-terms sum	Fraction picture

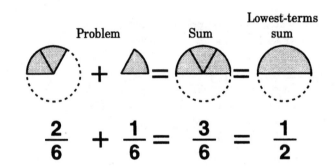

$$\frac{1}{4} + \frac{1}{4} = \frac{\square}{\square} = \frac{\square}{\square} \bigcirc$$

$$\frac{5}{8} + \frac{1}{8} = \frac{\square}{\square} = \frac{\square}{\square} \bigcirc$$

$$\frac{3}{12} + \frac{6}{12} = \frac{\square}{\square} = \frac{\square}{\square} \bigcirc$$

Sums Greater Than 1

Name_____

➤ Use two sets of fraction circles to find each sum.
➤ Draw a picture of the lowest-terms mixed number sum.

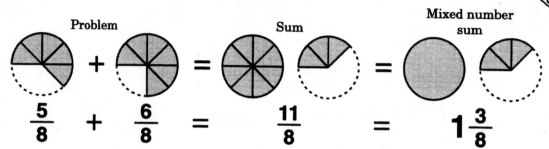

Problem   Sum   Mixed number sum

$$\frac{5}{8} + \frac{6}{8} = \frac{11}{8} = 1\frac{3}{8}$$

	Problem	Mixed number sum	Fraction picture

$$\frac{2}{3} + \frac{2}{3} = \underline{}\;\bigcirc\bigcirc$$

$$\frac{3}{5} + \frac{4}{5} = \underline{}\;\bigcirc\bigcirc$$

$$\frac{2}{4} + \frac{3}{4} = \underline{}\;\bigcirc\bigcirc$$

$$\frac{7}{12} + \frac{10}{12} = \underline{}\;\bigcirc\bigcirc$$

➤ For the following, find the lowest-terms sum.

$$\frac{3}{4} + \frac{3}{4} = \underline{}\;\bigcirc\bigcirc$$

$$\frac{5}{8} + \frac{7}{8} = \underline{}\;\bigcirc\bigcirc$$

$$\frac{9}{12} + \frac{7}{12} = \underline{}\;\bigcirc\bigcirc$$

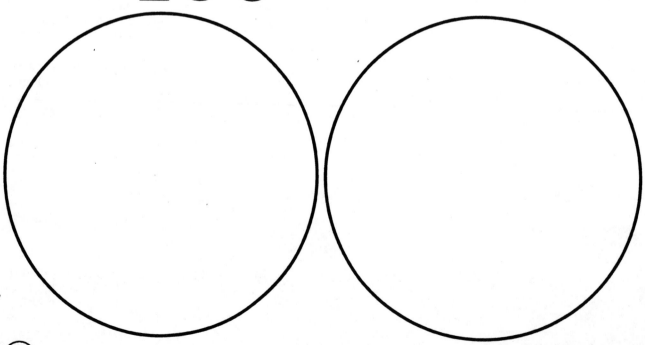

What Do We Have In Common?

Name_____

➤ Find common same-color fraction circle pieces for each pair of figures below.

Problem 1

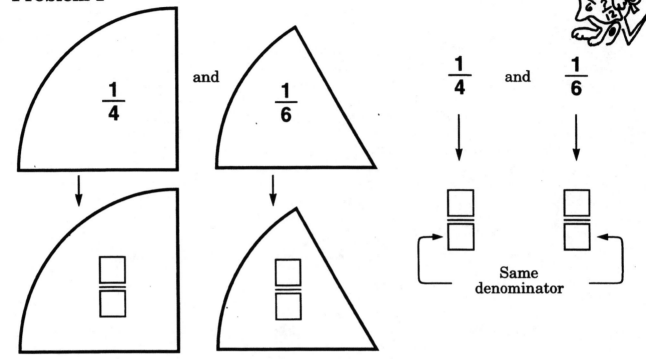

Problem 2

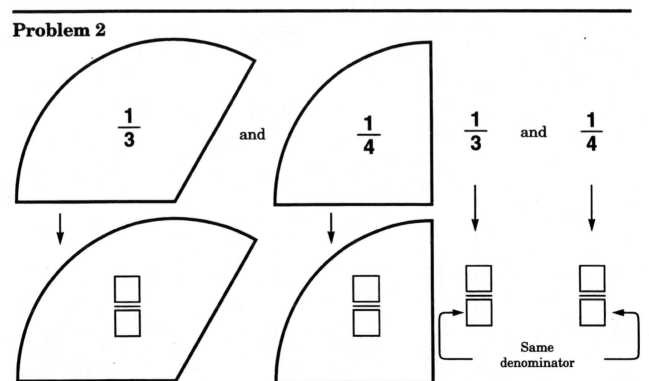

Add the Fractions: Unlike Denominators

Name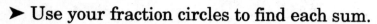

➤ Use your fraction circles to find each sum.

➤ Draw a fraction picture to show your work.

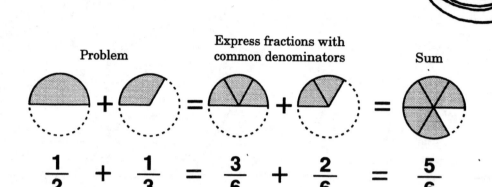

	Problem		Express fractions with common denominators		Sum

$$\frac{1}{2} + \frac{1}{3} = \frac{3}{6} + \frac{2}{6} = \frac{5}{6}$$

Problem	Express fractions with common denominators	Sum	Fraction picture

$$\frac{1}{2} + \frac{1}{4} = \frac{2}{4} + \frac{1}{4} = \frac{3}{4} \quad \bigcirc$$

$$\frac{2}{3} + \frac{1}{6} = \frac{\square}{\square} + \frac{\square}{\square} = \frac{\square}{\square} \quad \bigcirc$$

$$\frac{1}{4} + \frac{3}{8} = \frac{\square}{\square} + \frac{\square}{\square} = \frac{\square}{\square} \quad \bigcirc$$

$$\frac{1}{2} + \frac{1}{5} = \frac{\square}{\square} + \frac{\square}{\square} = \frac{\square}{\square} \quad \bigcirc$$

$$\frac{3}{4} + \frac{1}{6} = \frac{\square}{\square} + \frac{\square}{\square} = \frac{\square}{\square} \quad \bigcirc$$

$$\frac{2}{3} + \frac{1}{4} = \frac{\square}{\square} + \frac{\square}{\square} = \frac{\square}{\square} \quad \bigcirc$$

Add the Fractions: How Low Can You Go?

Name _____

➤ Use your fraction circles to find each sum in lowest terms.
➤ Draw a fraction picture to show your work.

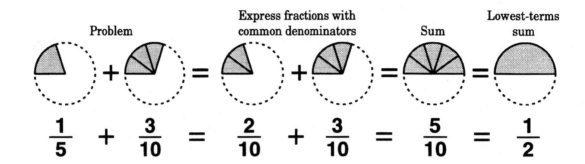

	Problem	Express fractions with common denominators		Sum		Lowest-terms sum
	$\dfrac{1}{5}$ + $\dfrac{3}{10}$	= $\dfrac{2}{10}$ + $\dfrac{3}{10}$	=	$\dfrac{5}{10}$	=	$\dfrac{1}{2}$

Problem	Express fractions with common denominators	Sum	Fraction picture	Lowest-terms sum	Lowest-terms fraction picture
$\dfrac{1}{4} + \dfrac{3}{12}$	$= \dfrac{\square}{\square} + \dfrac{\square}{\square}$	$= \dfrac{\square}{\square}$	◯	$= \dfrac{\square}{\square}$	◯
$\dfrac{1}{10} + \dfrac{2}{5}$	$= \dfrac{\square}{\square} + \dfrac{\square}{\square}$	$= \dfrac{\square}{\square}$	◯	$= \dfrac{\square}{\square}$	◯
$\dfrac{2}{3} + \dfrac{2}{12}$	$= \dfrac{\square}{\square} + \dfrac{\square}{\square}$	$= \dfrac{\square}{\square}$	◯	$= \dfrac{\square}{\square}$	◯
$\dfrac{1}{2} + \dfrac{1}{6}$	$= \dfrac{\square}{\square} + \dfrac{\square}{\square}$	$= \dfrac{\square}{\square}$	◯	$= \dfrac{\square}{\square}$	◯
$\dfrac{1}{12} + \dfrac{2}{3}$	$= \dfrac{\square}{\square} + \dfrac{\square}{\square}$	$= \dfrac{\square}{\square}$	◯	$= \dfrac{\square}{\square}$	◯
$\dfrac{1}{6} + \dfrac{1}{3}$	$= \dfrac{\square}{\square} + \dfrac{\square}{\square}$	$= \dfrac{\square}{\square}$	◯	$= \dfrac{\square}{\square}$	◯

More Sums Greater Than 1

Name_____

➤ Use two sets of fraction circles to find each sum. Express each sum as a lowest-terms mixed number. Draw a fraction picture to show your work.

Problem	Express fractions with common denominators	Sum	Mixed number sum

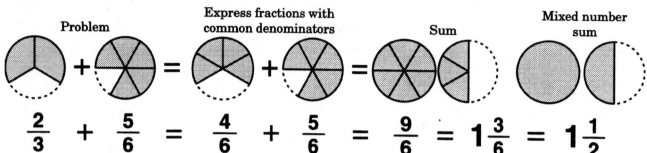

$$\frac{2}{3} \ + \ \frac{5}{6} \ = \ \frac{4}{6} \ + \ \frac{5}{6} \ = \ \frac{9}{6} \ = \ 1\frac{3}{6} \ = \ 1\frac{1}{2}$$

Problem	Express fractions with common denominators	Sum	Mixed number sum	Fraction picture

$$\frac{1}{4} + \frac{7}{8} \quad = \frac{\square}{\square} + \frac{\square}{\square} = \frac{\square}{\square} = \ \_\bigcirc\bigcirc$$

$$\frac{5}{6} + \frac{1}{3} \quad = \frac{\square}{\square} + \frac{\square}{\square} = \frac{\square}{\square} = \ \_\bigcirc\bigcirc$$

$$\frac{3}{5} + \frac{7}{10} \quad = \frac{\square}{\square} + \frac{\square}{\square} = \frac{\square}{\square} = \ \_\bigcirc\bigcirc$$

$$\frac{1}{2} + \frac{3}{4} \quad = \frac{\square}{\square} + \frac{\square}{\square} = \frac{\square}{\square} = \ \_\bigcirc\bigcirc$$

$$\frac{7}{12} + \frac{2}{3} \quad = \frac{\square}{\square} + \frac{\square}{\square} = \frac{\square}{\square} = \ \_\bigcirc\bigcirc$$

$$\frac{3}{5} + \frac{9}{10} \quad = \frac{\square}{\square} + \frac{\square}{\square} = \frac{\square}{\square} = \ \_\bigcirc\bigcirc$$

Make Sums of 1

Name_____

➤ Use your fraction circles to find the missing fractions.

➤ Draw the fraction picture.

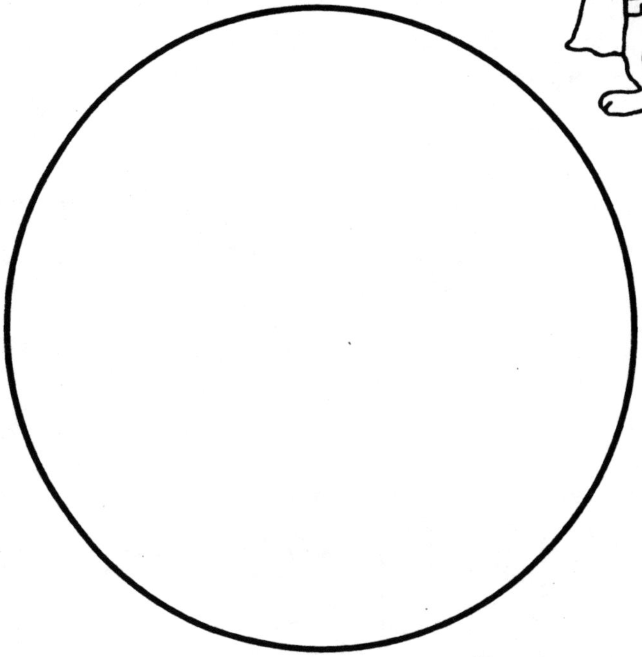

Fraction picture

$\dfrac{2}{3} + \dfrac{\Box}{3} = 1$ (·)

$\dfrac{2}{3} + \dfrac{\Box}{6} = 1$ (·)

$\dfrac{2}{3} + \dfrac{\Box}{12} = 1$ (·)

$\dfrac{\Box}{4} + \dfrac{3}{4} = 1$ (·)

$\dfrac{3}{4} + \dfrac{\Box}{8} = 1$ (·)

$\dfrac{\Box}{12} + \dfrac{3}{4} = 1$ (·)

Fraction picture

$\dfrac{1}{2} + \dfrac{\Box}{4} = 1$ (·)

$\dfrac{1}{2} + \dfrac{\Box}{2} = 1$ (·)

$\dfrac{\Box}{10} + \dfrac{1}{2} = 1$ (·)

$\dfrac{1}{2} + \dfrac{\Box}{6} = 1$ (·)

$\dfrac{\Box}{8} + \dfrac{1}{2} = 1$ (·)

Subtracting Fractions: Common Denominators

Name_____

➤ Use your fraction circles with arrows to find each difference.

➤ Draw a fraction picture with arrows to show your work.

Problem   Difference

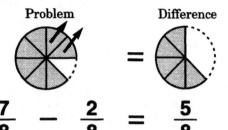

$$\frac{7}{8} \; - \; \frac{2}{8} \; = \; \frac{5}{8}$$

Problem	Difference	Fraction picture

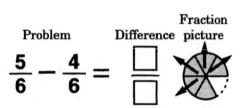

$$\frac{5}{6} - \frac{4}{6} = \frac{\square}{\square}$$

$$\frac{7}{8} - \frac{4}{8} = \frac{\square}{\square}$$

$$\frac{4}{5} - \frac{1}{5} = \frac{\square}{\square}$$

$$\frac{9}{10} - \frac{6}{10} = \frac{\square}{\square}$$

$$\frac{7}{12} - \frac{2}{12} = \frac{\square}{\square}$$

$$\frac{5}{8} - \frac{4}{8} = \frac{\square}{\square}$$

$$\frac{4}{5} - \frac{2}{5} = \frac{\square}{\square}$$

➤ Express each difference as a lowest-terms fraction.

Problem   Difference   Lowest-terms difference

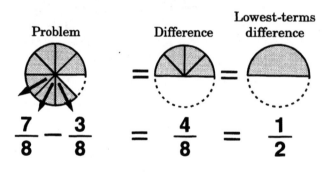

$$\frac{7}{8} \; - \; \frac{3}{8} \; = \; \frac{4}{8} \; = \; \frac{1}{2}$$

$$\frac{3}{4} - \frac{1}{4} = \frac{\square}{\square} = \frac{\square}{\square}$$

$$\frac{5}{6} - \frac{1}{6} = \frac{\square}{\square} = \frac{\square}{\square}$$

$$\frac{7}{12} - \frac{5}{12} = \frac{\square}{\square} = \frac{\square}{\square}$$

Fractions in Action
© 1994 Learning Resources, Inc.

Subtracting Fractions: Unlike Denominators

Name_____

➤ Use your fraction circles to find common denominators before you subtract.

➤ Express the difference in lowest-terms.

Problem → Express fractions with common denominators = Difference = Lowest-terms difference

$$\frac{2}{3} - \frac{1}{6} = \frac{4}{6} - \frac{1}{6} = \frac{3}{6} = \frac{1}{2}$$

Problem — Express fractions with common denominators — Difference

$$\frac{1}{2} - \frac{3}{8} = \frac{\square}{\square} - \frac{\square}{\square} = \frac{\square}{\square} \bigcirc$$

$$\frac{5}{8} - \frac{1}{4} = \frac{\square}{\square} - \frac{\square}{\square} = \frac{\square}{\square} \bigcirc$$

$$\frac{4}{5} - \frac{7}{10} = \frac{\square}{\square} - \frac{\square}{\square} = \frac{\square}{\square} \bigcirc$$

Lowest-terms difference — Lowest-terms fraction picture

$$\frac{2}{3} - \frac{5}{12} = \frac{\square}{\square} - \frac{\square}{\square} = \frac{\square}{\square} \bigcirc = \frac{\square}{\square} \bigcirc$$

$$\frac{5}{6} - \frac{1}{2} = \frac{\square}{\square} - \frac{\square}{\square} = \frac{\square}{\square} \bigcirc = \frac{\square}{\square} \bigcirc$$

$$\frac{2}{3} - \frac{5}{12} = \frac{\square}{\square} - \frac{\square}{\square} = \frac{\square}{\square} \bigcirc = \frac{\square}{\square} \bigcirc$$

Subtract from Mixed Numbers

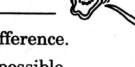

Name_____

➤ Use two sets of fraction circles to find each difference.

➤ Express the difference in lowest terms when possible.

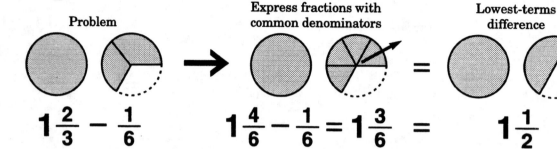

Problem	Express fractions with common denominators	Difference	Lowest-terms difference	Lowest-terms fraction picture

$1\frac{3}{4} - \frac{3}{8}$ = $1\frac{\square}{\square} - \frac{\square}{\square}$ = ___

$1\frac{1}{2} - \frac{2}{5}$ = $1\frac{\square}{\square} - \frac{\square}{\square}$ = ___

$1\frac{3}{4} - \frac{5}{8}$ = $1\frac{\square}{\square} - \frac{\square}{\square}$ = ___

$1\frac{2}{3} - \frac{5}{12}$ = $1\frac{\square}{\square} - \frac{\square}{\square}$ = ___ = ___

$1\frac{5}{6} - \frac{7}{12}$ = $1\frac{\square}{\square} - \frac{\square}{\square}$ = ___ = ___

$1\frac{4}{5} - \frac{1}{2}$ = $1\frac{\square}{\square} - \frac{\square}{\square}$ = ___

Fractions in Action
© 1994 Learning Resources, Inc.

Regroup to Subtract

➤ Use two sets of fraction circles to find each difference.

➤ Express the difference in lowest terms when possible.

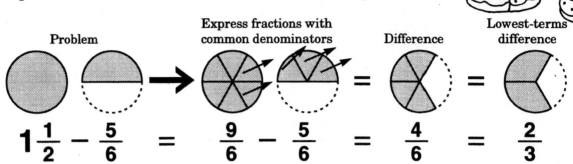

	Problem		Express fractions with common denominators		Difference		Lowest-terms difference
	$1\frac{1}{2}$	$-\frac{5}{6}$	$=$	$\frac{9}{6} - \frac{5}{6}$	$=$	$\frac{4}{6}$	$= \frac{2}{3}$

Change mixed number to improper fraction

Problem	Express fractions with common denominators	Difference	Lowest-terms difference	Lowest-terms fraction picture

$1\frac{1}{4} - \frac{1}{2}$ = $\dfrac{\square}{\square} - \dfrac{\square}{\square}$ = ___   (·) (·)

$1\frac{3}{5} - \frac{7}{10}$ = $\dfrac{\square}{\square} - \dfrac{\square}{\square}$ = ___   (·) (·)

$1\frac{5}{8} - \frac{3}{4}$ = $\dfrac{\square}{\square} - \dfrac{\square}{\square}$ = ___   (·) (·)

$1 - \frac{4}{6}$ = $\dfrac{\square}{\square} - \dfrac{\square}{\square}$ = ___ = ___   (·) (·)

$2 - \frac{5}{8}$ = $1\dfrac{\square}{\square} - \dfrac{\square}{\square}$ = ___   (·) (·)

$1\frac{1}{3} - \frac{5}{6}$ = $\dfrac{\square}{\square} - \dfrac{\square}{\square}$ = ___ = ___   (·) (·)

Multiply with Unit Fractions

Name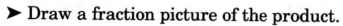_____

➤ Find the fraction circle that fits each unit, and label it with a fraction. Then multiply the fraction by the whole number.

➤ Draw a fraction picture of the product.

5 of 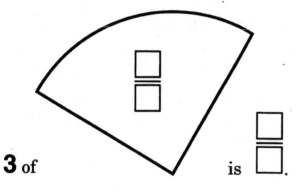 is ☐. It looks like this. ➔

3 of 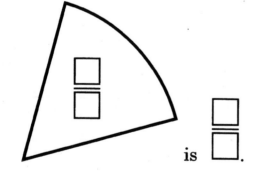 is ☐. It looks like this. ➔

4 of is ☐. It looks like this. ➔

9 of 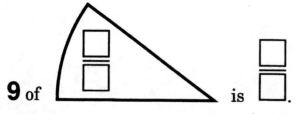 is ☐. It looks like this. ➔

Fractions in Action
© 1994 Learning Resources, Inc.

Multiply Fractions and Whole Numbers

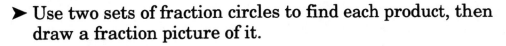

Name_____

➤ Use two sets of fraction circles to find each product, then draw a fraction picture of it.

Problem	Meaning: Repeated addition		Product		Lowest-terms product

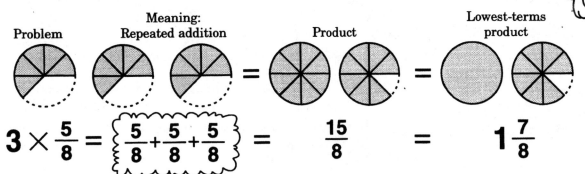

$$3 \times \frac{5}{8} = \left\{ \frac{5}{8} + \frac{5}{8} + \frac{5}{8} \right\} = \frac{15}{8} = 1\frac{7}{8}$$

Problem	Meaning: Repeated addition	Lowest-terms product	Fraction picture
$4 \times \dfrac{1}{5} \;=$		$=$ ___	⊙ ⊙
$3 \times \dfrac{2}{3} \;=$		$=$ ___	⊙ ⊙
$3 \times \dfrac{2}{5} \;=$		$=$ ___	⊙ ⊙
$^*4 \times \dfrac{3}{8} \;=$		$=$ ___	⊙ ⊙
$^*2 \times \dfrac{5}{6} \;=$		$=$ ___	⊙ ⊙
$^*5 \times \dfrac{3}{10} \;=$		$=$ ___	⊙ ⊙

*Find lowest terms.

Fractions in Action

Multiply Fractions

Name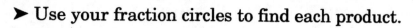

➤ Use your fraction circles to find each product.

	Meaning	Product	
			Here's another way to solve the problem. Make a cutout of $\frac{3}{4}$ of a circle. Fold it in half. Then find a fraction circle that matches a half of $\frac{3}{4}$.
$\frac{3}{4}$	$\frac{1}{2}$ of $\frac{3}{4}$ = $\frac{3}{8}$		

Problem	Meaning	Product	Fraction picture
$\frac{1}{2}$ of $\frac{4}{5}$	◯	= ▢/▢	◯
$\frac{1}{3}$ of $\frac{1}{2}$	◯	= ▢/▢	◯
$\frac{1}{2}$ of $\frac{5}{6}$	◯	= ▢/▢	◯
$\frac{1}{2}$ of $\frac{2}{3}$	◯	= ▢/▢	◯
* $\frac{1}{3}$ of $\frac{6}{10}$	◯	= ▢/▢	◯
* $\frac{1}{4}$ of $\frac{2}{3}$	◯	= ▢/▢	◯

*Find lowest terms.

How Many Can Cover?

➤ Use your fraction circles to find each quotient. Think: "How many times will the divisor cover the dividend?"

$$\frac{1}{2} \div \frac{1}{6}$$

means

How many $\frac{1}{6}$s can cover $\frac{1}{2}$?

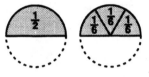 Cover $\frac{1}{2}$ with $\frac{1}{6}$s.

$$\frac{1}{2} \div \frac{1}{6} = 3$$

It takes 3 of the $\frac{1}{6}$ pieces to cover $\frac{1}{2}$.

➤ Fill in the blanks. Then find the quotients.

$1 \div \frac{1}{2}$ means: How many _____ can cover _____ ? Answer: _____

$\frac{3}{4} \div \frac{1}{4}$ means: How many _____ can cover _____ ? Answer: _____

$\frac{1}{2} \div \frac{1}{8}$ means: How many _____ can cover _____ ? Answer: _____

$\frac{4}{5} \div \frac{1}{10}$ means: How many _____ can cover _____ ? Answer: _____

$\frac{2}{3} \div \frac{1}{6}$ means: How many _____ can cover _____ ? Answer: _____

How Many Can Cover Again?

Name_____

▶ Use your fraction circles to find each quotient. Think: "How many times will the divisor cover the dividend?"

$$\frac{1}{2} \div \frac{1}{3}$$

means

How many $\frac{1}{3}$s can cover $\frac{1}{2}$?

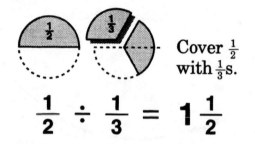 Cover $\frac{1}{2}$ with $\frac{1}{3}$s.

$$\frac{1}{2} \div \frac{1}{3} = 1\frac{1}{2}$$

It takes $1\frac{1}{2}$ of the $\frac{1}{3}$ pieces to cover $\frac{1}{2}$.

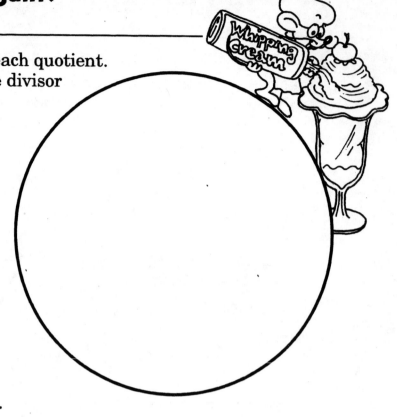

▶ Fill in the blanks. Then find the quotients.

$\frac{1}{2} \div \frac{1}{4}$ means: How many _____ can cover _____ ? Answer: _____

$\frac{1}{4} \div \frac{1}{2}$ means: How many _____ can cover _____ ? Answer: _____

$\frac{3}{4} \div \frac{1}{2}$ means: How many _____ can cover _____ ? Answer: _____

$1 \div \frac{2}{3}$ means: How many _____ can cover _____ ? Answer: _____

$\frac{5}{6} \div \frac{1}{3}$ means: How many _____ can cover _____ ? Answer: _____

It's About Time

Name_____

➤ Use your fraction circles on the clock face below to figure out the number of minutes for a fraction of an hour.

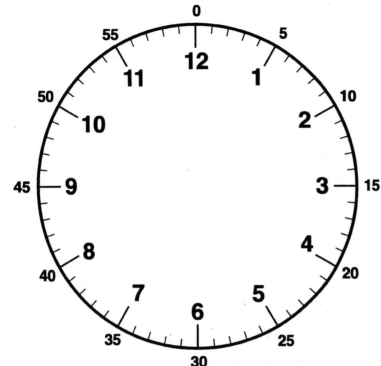

1 hour = 60 minutes

$\frac{1}{2}$ hour = 30 minutes

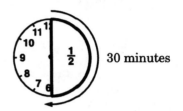

30 minutes

➤ Cover the clock face with the following fraction circles. Tell how many minutes are covered, and then draw a fraction clock picture of the answer.

$\frac{1}{4}$ hour = _____ minutes

$\frac{3}{4}$ hour = _____ minutes

$\frac{1}{3}$ hour = _____ minutes

$\frac{2}{3}$ hour = _____ minutes

$\frac{1}{6}$ hour = _____ minutes

$\frac{2}{5}$ hour = _____ minutes

$\frac{1}{12}$ hour = _____ minutes

$\frac{5}{6}$ hour = _____ minutes

$\frac{1}{10}$ hour = _____ minutes

$\frac{11}{12}$ hour = _____ minutes

Spending Time Figuring Fractions

Name_____

➤ Use your fraction circles to figure out what fraction of the day and how many hours Dave spends on each activity.

Dave's Day
8:00 AM to 8:00 PM

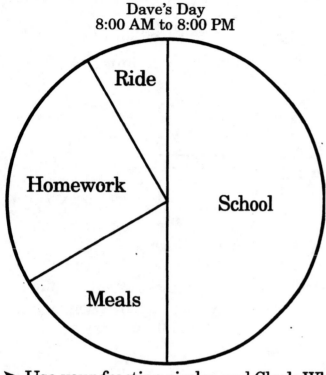

Dave's Activity	Fraction of Day	Hours of Activity
School day	_____	_____
Homework	_____	_____
Meals	_____	_____
Ride to and from school	_____	_____

➤ Use your fraction circles and Clock Wheel to figure out the fractional parts of Simone's Saturday. Make a circle graph to show how she spent her time from 9:00 AM to 9:00 PM.

Simone's Saturday

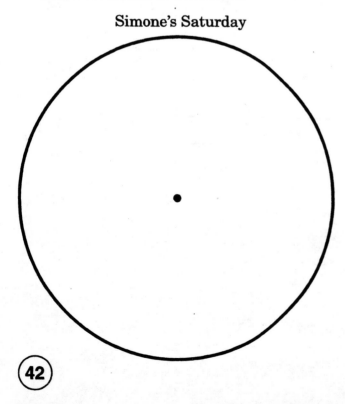

Simone's Activity	Hours of Activity	Fraction of Day
Go shopping 9:00–1:00	_____	_____
Eat lunch 1:00–2:00	_____	_____
Go to movie 2:00–4:00	_____	_____
Go on picnic 4:00–9:00	_____	_____

Fractions in Action
© 1994 Learning Resources, Inc.

Fractions Can Be Fun, To A Degree

Name_____

➤ Use your fraction circles and the Degree Wheel below to figure the number of degrees in a fraction of a complete revolution (360 degrees).

 $\frac{1}{4}$ of 360° is 90°

90° is the number of degrees in the central angle of this circle.

$\frac{1}{2}$ of 360° is ———.

$\frac{1}{3}$ of 360° is ———.

$\frac{1}{6}$ of 360° is ———.

$\frac{1}{12}$ of 360° is ———.

$\frac{1}{10}$ of 360° is ———.

$\frac{1}{8}$ of 360° is ———.

$\frac{1}{5}$ of 360° is ———.

$\frac{3}{4}$ of 360° is ———.

$\frac{2}{3}$ of 360° is ———.

$\frac{5}{12}$ of 360° is ———.

To Make a Degree Wheel
1. Cut out the two circles.
2. Cut along the "cut" lines to the center of each circle.
3. Fit the circles together.
4. Move the blank wheel around to show the number of degrees.

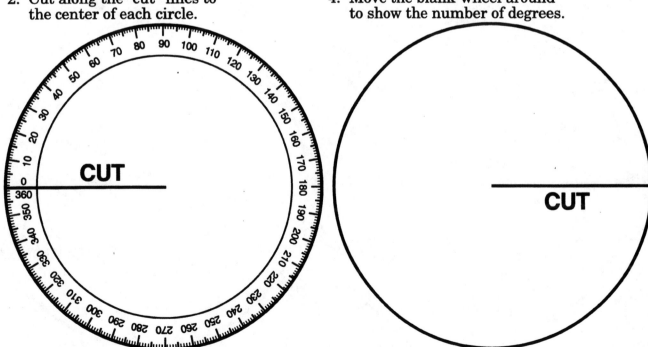

Fractions Are 100 Percent Fun!

Name_____

➤ Use your fraction circles and the Percent Wheel below to find percent equivalents for the following fractions.

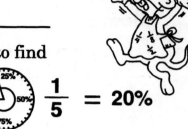 $\dfrac{1}{5} = 20\%$

$\dfrac{1}{2} = $ _____ % $\dfrac{2}{5} = $ _____ % $\dfrac{1}{6} = $ _____ %

$\dfrac{1}{4} = $ _____ % $\dfrac{1}{8} = $ _____ % $\dfrac{5}{6} = $ _____ %

$\dfrac{1}{10} = $ _____ % $\dfrac{3}{8} = $ _____ % $\dfrac{1}{12} = $ _____ %

$\dfrac{3}{4} = $ _____ % $\dfrac{1}{3} = $ _____ % $\dfrac{5}{12} = $ _____ %

$\dfrac{3}{10} = $ _____ % $\dfrac{2}{3} = $ _____ % $\dfrac{7}{12} = $ _____ %

To Make a Percent Wheel
1. Cut out the two circles.
2. Cut along the "cut" lines to the center of each circle.
3. Fit the circles together.
4. Move the blank wheel around to show the fraction and the percent.

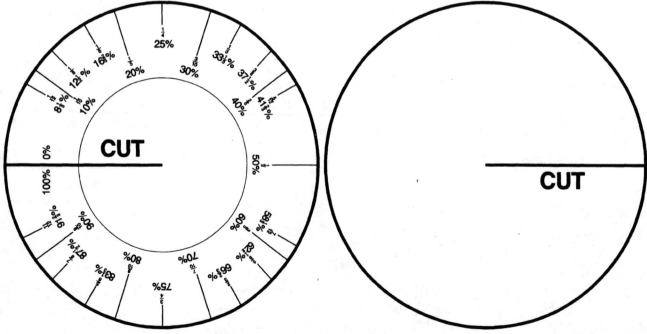

Fractions in Action
© 1994 Learning Resources, Inc.

What Do the Circle Graphs Say?

➤ Use your fraction circles, Degree Wheel, and Percent Wheel to figure out the size of each section below.

Student Field Trip

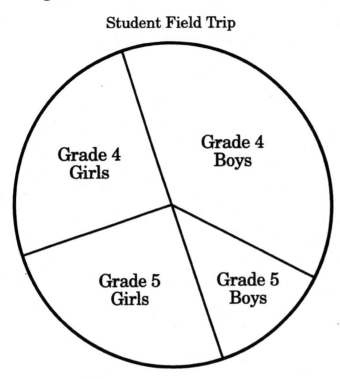

Students	Fraction	Percent	Degrees of Central Angle
Grade 4 Girls	_____	_____	_____
Grade 5 Girls	_____	_____	_____
Grade 4 Boys	_____	_____	_____
Grade 5 Boys	_____	_____	_____
Totals	1	100%	360°

Favorite Class Survey

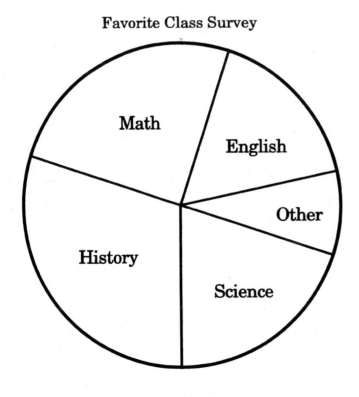

Favorite Class	Fraction	Percent	Degrees of Central Angle
Math	_____	_____	_____
History	_____	_____	_____
English	_____	_____	_____
Science	_____	_____	_____
Other	_____	_____	_____
Totals	1	100%	360°

Make Your Own Circle Graphs

Name_____

➤ Use your fraction circles, Degree Wheel, Percent Wheel, and the information below to construct each circle graph.

Symphony Orchestra

Type of Instrument	Fraction Part	Percent Part	Degrees of Central Angle
36 Strings	_____	_____	_____
18 Woodwinds	_____	_____	_____
12 Brass	_____	_____	_____
6 Percussion	_____	_____	_____
Totals _____	1	100%	360°

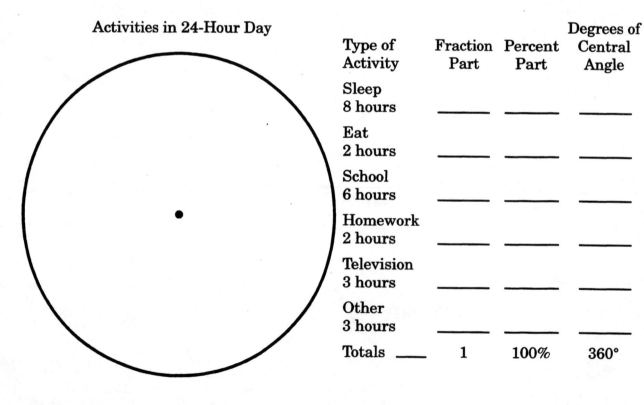

Activities in 24-Hour Day

Type of Activity	Fraction Part	Percent Part	Degrees of Central Angle
Sleep 8 hours	_____	_____	_____
Eat 2 hours	_____	_____	_____
School 6 hours	_____	_____	_____
Homework 2 hours	_____	_____	_____
Television 3 hours	_____	_____	_____
Other 3 hours	_____	_____	_____
Totals _____	1	100%	360°

Fractions in Action
© 1994 Learning Resources, Inc.

Rainbow Fraction Squares
Teaching Notes

Objectives

Use Deluxe Rainbow Fraction Squares:
- To model equivalent fractions and to compare fractions.
- To perform operations using fractions, whole numbers and mixed numbers.
- To relate fractions to decimals and percent.

Warm Up

Have students fold, color, and label 4-inch (10×10 cm) squares of paper into halves, thirds, fourths, sixths, and eighths. Distribute colored pencils or crayons and six 4-inch squares of paper to each student and ask them to do the following:

1. Color one whole square red.
2. Fold one square in half. Color one-half pink and label it $\frac{1}{2}$.
3. Fold one square in half, then in half again. Color one-fourth yellow and label it $\frac{1}{4}$.
4. Fold one square in half three times to yield eighths. Color one-eighth blue and label it $\frac{1}{8}$.
5. Fold one square into three equal parts. Color one-third orange and label it $\frac{1}{3}$.
6. Fold one square into thirds, then in half into sixths. Color one-sixth teal and label it $\frac{1}{6}$.

Ask the students to show $\frac{1}{12}$ or $\frac{1}{5}$ or $\frac{1}{10}$. Distribute more squares of paper to make the twelfths (black), fifths (green), and tenths (purple). This activity gives students insight into the set of fraction squares. Distribute sets of the Deluxe Rainbow Fraction Squares to compare them with the handmade fraction squares.

Ask how a large square cake or casserole dish might be divided evenly among a pair or a small group of students. Have students draw a square cake on an $8\frac{1}{2}'' \times 11''$ sheet of paper. Call on various students to show halves, fourths, eighths, thirds, sixths, or twelfths by making folds in their food picture and cutting apart the fractional parts. Ask the students to compare the fractional parts with each other.

Fraction Square Materials

Deluxe Rainbow Fraction Squares (LER 619)
Deluxe Overhead Rainbow Fraction Squares (LER 620)
Blackline masters on pages 50–53

Using the Activity Pages

Naming Fractions *(page 54)*

Students match their Rainbow Fraction Square pieces to the outlines on page 54 to identify and name the fraction pieces. As a prelude to page 55, ask them to find how many of each unit fraction are needed to fill a unit square.

Names for 1 *(page 55)*

Students are to show the various representations ($\frac{n}{n}$) for the value of 1 (i.e., $1 = \frac{2}{2}$ or $1 = \frac{5}{5}$). The last exercise helps students include fractions constructed from the fraction square pieces. For example, students could show that 9 ninths equals 1 by making a fraction square model for $\frac{1}{3}$ and then folding each $\frac{1}{3}$ piece in thirds to make $\frac{1}{9}$ pieces.

Equivalent Fractions (page 56)

In order for students to find an equivalent fraction, use other same-color fraction square pieces. Follow these steps: (1) Place the fraction square pieces on the unit square, and (2) find other same-color fraction square pieces to completely cover the fraction.

Naming and Comparing Fractions
(pages 57–58)

Pages 57 and 58 were designed to be used together. Students identify the different fraction sections in each figure, then subdivide remaining sections to show smaller fraction parts. Students are to compare various fraction sections to each other. Some students may wish to cut out the fractions sections to verify their answers.

Improper Fractions to Mixed Numbers (page 59)

Students will need at least three sets of Rainbow Fraction Squares for this activity page. Since the unit squares are quite large, the students will have to use their desks as a workspace when using their fraction squares. Have the students express the improper fraction as a mixed number by writing the mixed number and drawing a picture of it in the three small squares next to the answer blank.

Students should draw their pictures using all unit fraction pieces. For example, $\frac{8}{3}$ can be shown as $\frac{3}{3}$ and $\frac{3}{3}$ and $\frac{2}{3}$ to find the mixed number $2\frac{2}{3}$. Remind them to find the lowest-terms mixed number for an improper fraction.

Adding Fractions (pages 60–62)

On page 60, students are to find the sum of two fractions having common denominators. Before assigning pages 60 and 61, have them find common denomi-

nators for pairs of fractions with unlike denominators. (Refer back to the technique used on page 27 with fraction circles.) On pages 61 and 62, students find the sum of fractions with unlike denominators.

Page 62 differs from page 61 in that the sums are greater than one. Remind students to use two sets of fraction squares to find each sum. Also, have students express each sum in lowest terms when possible.

Note: The processes for adding, subtracting, multiplying, and dividing fractions are the same whether the students are using fraction circles, squares, or tiles. Refer to the explanations and examples using the fraction circle pieces in Teaching Notes, pages 7–11.

Subtracting Fractions (pages 63–64)

Page 63 contains fractions with common denominators. Page 64 contains fractions with unlike denominators. Examples are provided at the top of each page to show the subtraction process.

Multiplying Fractions (pages 65–66)

Students multiply a fraction by a whole number and a fraction by a unit fraction, respectively. Suggest that students work in groups because they will need at least three sets of fraction squares to find the products. Urge students to estimate answers to the problems. On page 66, students will discover that a fractional part of a fraction is smaller than the original part.

For example, $\frac{1}{2}$ of $\frac{3}{4}$ is actually $\frac{3}{4}$ being cut in half to yield $\frac{3}{8}$. Students must think in terms of equivalent fractions for $\frac{3}{4}$ [i.e., $\frac{6}{8}$ or $\frac{9}{12}$] in order to find half of the area covered by $\frac{3}{4}$. When students choose $\frac{6}{8}$ as the equivalent fraction for $\frac{3}{4}$ then it is quite easy to show that $\frac{1}{2}$ of $\frac{6}{8}$ is $\frac{3}{8}$.

Dividing Fractions *(pages 67–68)*

Students will practice dividing 1 by a fraction or a fraction by a fraction. The exercises focus on division by using familiar commonplace fractions. Ask whether the quotient will be less than, greater than, or equal to 1. All quotients for the problems on page 66 will be greater than 1 since each divisor is smaller than the dividend.

For the last problem on page 67, students can save themselves a lot of work if they recognize that $\frac{5}{10}$ is equivalent to $\frac{1}{2}$, and then figure out that $\frac{1}{2}$ divided by itself is 1. On page 68, the quotient for $\frac{1}{2} \div \frac{3}{4}$ will be less than 1 since a smaller number is being divided by a larger number.

Fraction Connection to Decimals

(page 69)

Warm Up: Distribute seven 10-cm square pieces of green paper each to groups of four students. Tell them that this is a square dollar bill. Have them cut them into 2 pieces ($\frac{1}{2}$, *half dollar, $0.50*), 4 pieces ($\frac{1}{4}$, *quarter, $0.25*), 10 pieces ($\frac{1}{10}$, *dime, $0.10*), 20 pieces ($\frac{1}{20}$, *nickel, $0.05*), 100 pieces ($\frac{1}{100}$, *penny, $0.01*), and to leave one square piece as a whole dollar bill. Instruct them to use the same configurations as the fraction square pieces for halves, fourths, fifths, tenths, and hundredths, as they cut apart the green square pieces of paper into smaller denominations. Discuss the relationship between the fraction square pieces and the amounts of money (expressed in dollar notation; i.e., $0.50).

When completing the exercises on page 69, remind students that the 10 × 10 grid shown on the page could represent 100 cents, or that each small square is $\frac{1}{100}$ of the unit square. Warn students that when finding decimal equivalents for fractions such as $\frac{1}{8}$ or $\frac{1}{3}$, they will have to estimate halves and thirds of the small squares when counting up all the squares to represent a given fraction in hundredths.

Fraction Connection to Percent

(page 70)

Percent is another way to talk about hundredths. Use the fraction square pieces with the 10 × 10 cm grid on page 70 to show that percent means "per 100." The Warm Up activity and the exercises dealing with decimals should be a natural transition into learning about and expressing fractions as percents.

Wrap Up

Performance evaluation. Ask students to show how to express an improper fraction as a lowest-terms mixed number, and to find the sum of two fractions.

Written assessment. Ask students to write how they would cut up a square birthday cake for 24 members of a class. Ask older students to write about the connection between fractions, decimals or percent using the fraction square pieces and a 10 × 10 cm grid. Have students determine what decimal and percent part of the birthday cake is equivalent to each fraction piece eaten by the student.

Fraction Squares

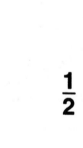

One: Red

1

Halves: Pink

$\frac{1}{2}$

Fourths: Yellow

$\frac{1}{4}$ $\frac{1}{4}$ $\frac{1}{4}$ $\frac{1}{4}$

$\frac{1}{2}$

Fractions in Action
© 1994 Learning Resources, Inc.

Fraction Squares

Thirds: Orange

$\dfrac{1}{3}$
$\dfrac{1}{3}$
$\dfrac{1}{3}$

Twelfths: Black

$\dfrac{1}{12}$	$\dfrac{1}{12}$
$\dfrac{1}{12}$	$\dfrac{1}{12}$
$\dfrac{1}{12}$	$\dfrac{1}{12}$

Sixths: Teal

$\dfrac{1}{6}$	$\dfrac{1}{6}$
$\dfrac{1}{6}$	$\dfrac{1}{6}$
$\dfrac{1}{6}$	$\dfrac{1}{6}$

$\dfrac{1}{12}$	$\dfrac{1}{12}$
$\dfrac{1}{12}$	$\dfrac{1}{12}$
$\dfrac{1}{12}$	$\dfrac{1}{12}$

Fraction Squares

Fifths: Green

$\dfrac{1}{5}$
$\dfrac{1}{5}$
$\dfrac{1}{5}$
$\dfrac{1}{5}$
$\dfrac{1}{5}$

Eighths: Blue

$\dfrac{1}{8}$	$\dfrac{1}{8}$
$\dfrac{1}{8}$	$\dfrac{1}{8}$

Tenths: Purple

$\dfrac{1}{10}$	$\dfrac{1}{10}$
$\dfrac{1}{10}$	$\dfrac{1}{10}$
$\dfrac{1}{10}$	$\dfrac{1}{10}$
$\dfrac{1}{10}$	$\dfrac{1}{10}$
$\dfrac{1}{10}$	$\dfrac{1}{10}$

$\dfrac{1}{8}$	$\dfrac{1}{8}$
$\dfrac{1}{8}$	$\dfrac{1}{8}$

Fractions in Action
© 1994 Learning Resources, Inc.

Fraction Squares

One

Hundredths

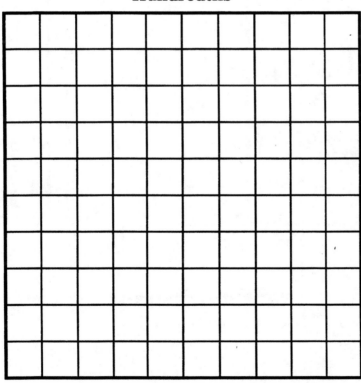

Name It With A Fraction!

Name_____

➤ Use your fraction squares to determine the fraction for each piece, then label it.

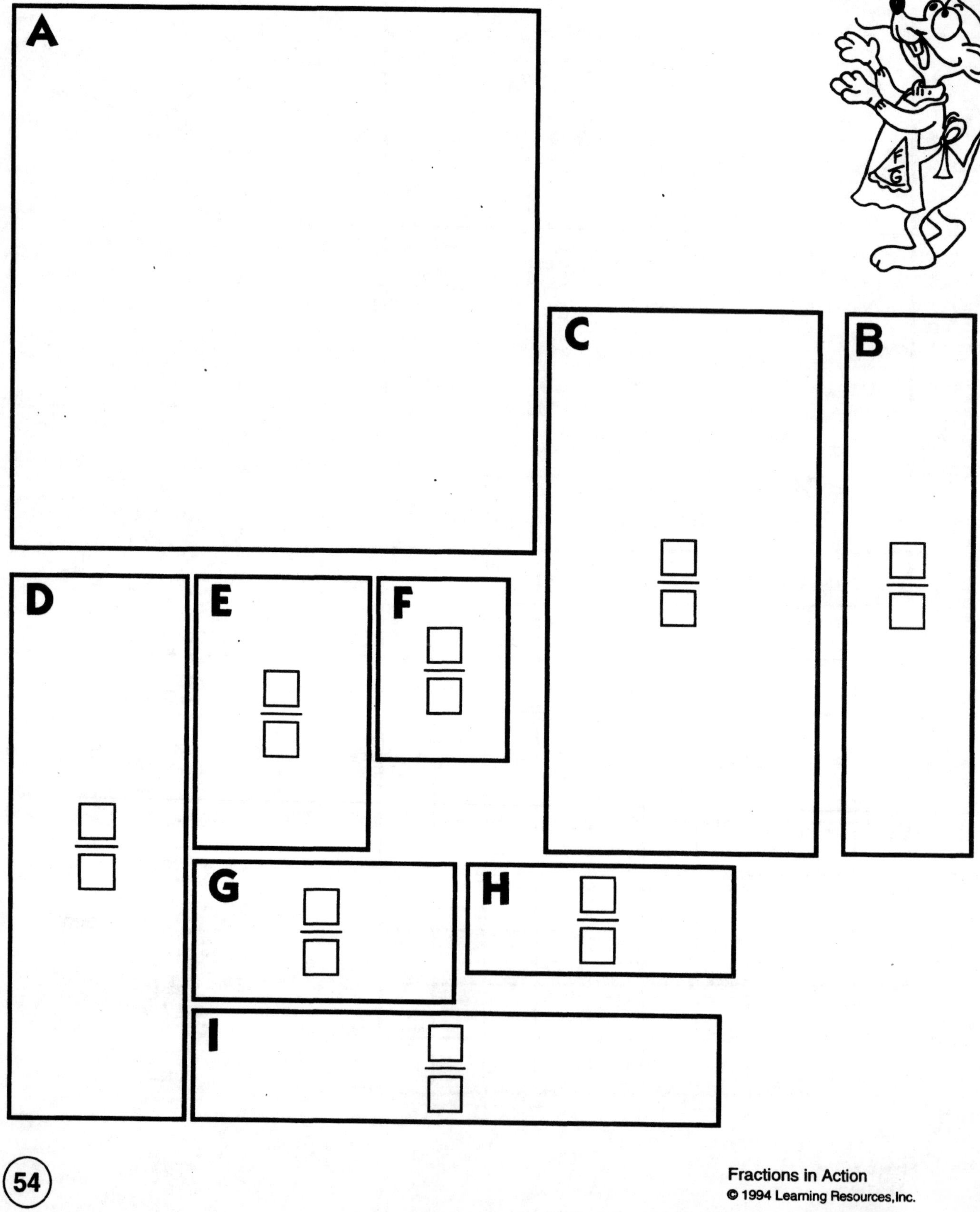

A

C

B $\dfrac{\Box}{\Box}$

$\dfrac{\Box}{\Box}$

D $\dfrac{\Box}{\Box}$

E $\dfrac{\Box}{\Box}$

F $\dfrac{\Box}{\Box}$

G $\dfrac{\Box}{\Box}$

H $\dfrac{\Box}{\Box}$

I $\dfrac{\Box}{\Box}$

Fractions in Action
© 1994 Learning Resources, Inc.

One-Color Cover

Name_____

➤ Use your fraction squares to find how many of the same-color pieces cover the unit square exactly.

$$= \frac{\square}{2} \quad \frac{\square}{3}$$

$$\frac{\square}{4} \quad \frac{\square}{5}$$

$$\frac{\square}{6} \quad \frac{\square}{8}$$

$$\frac{\square}{10} \quad \frac{\square}{12}$$

➤ Use the information you gathered above to find the fractions equivalent to 1.

$$1 = \frac{\square}{\boxed{2}} = \frac{\boxed{3}}{\boxed{3}} = \frac{\boxed{4}}{\square} = \frac{\square}{\square} = \frac{\square}{\square} = \frac{\square}{\boxed{8}} = \frac{\boxed{10}}{\square} = \frac{\square}{\boxed{12}}$$

➤ Did you notice a pattern above? Can you fill in the numerators?

$$1 = \frac{\square}{9} = \frac{\square}{15} = \frac{\square}{16} = \frac{\square}{20} = \frac{\square}{24} = \frac{\square}{25} = \frac{\square}{32} = \frac{\square}{64}$$

Cover-Up

Name_____

➤ Place your fraction squares on the unit square here to find equivalent fractions for each of the fractions below.

$$\frac{1}{2} = \frac{\square}{12}$$

➤ Place the $\frac{1}{2}$ piece on the unit square.

➤ Then cover the $\frac{1}{2}$ piece with $\frac{1}{12}$ pieces so that the $\frac{1}{2}$ piece is covered completely.

$$\frac{1}{3} = \frac{\square}{6} \qquad \frac{1}{4} = \frac{\square}{12} \qquad \frac{2}{5} = \frac{\square}{10} \qquad \frac{8}{12} = \frac{\square}{3}$$

$$\frac{5}{10} = \frac{\square}{2} \qquad \frac{3}{4} = \frac{\square}{12} \qquad \frac{2}{6} = \frac{4}{\square} \qquad \frac{2}{3} = \frac{\square}{12}$$

$$\frac{1}{\square} = \frac{2}{10} \qquad \frac{6}{12} = \frac{4}{\square} \qquad \frac{5}{6} = \frac{10}{\square} \qquad \frac{2}{8} = \frac{\square}{12}$$

Break Down the Box

➤ Use your fraction square pieces to name and label each part of the unit square. Then draw smaller fraction pieces.

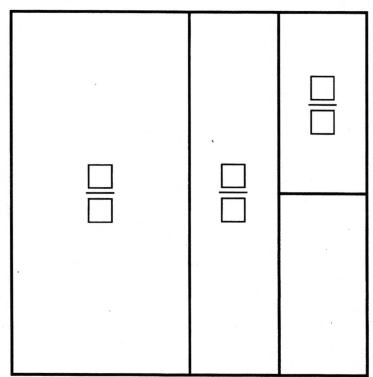

Compare. Write < or >.

$\frac{1}{2} \bigcirc \frac{1}{4}$ $\frac{1}{8} \bigcirc \frac{1}{4}$

➤ On the unlabeled fraction section, draw a line to show $\frac{1}{16}$ and label it. Then draw a line to show $\frac{1}{32}$ and label it.

Compare. Write < or >.

$\frac{1}{8} \bigcirc \frac{1}{16}$ $\frac{1}{32} \bigcirc \frac{1}{16}$

$\frac{1}{16} \bigcirc \frac{1}{4}$ $\frac{1}{32} \bigcirc \frac{1}{2}$

Compare. Write < or >.

$\frac{1}{3} \bigcirc \frac{1}{6}$ $\frac{1}{6} \bigcirc \frac{1}{12}$

➤ Choose one of the $\frac{1}{3}$ sections to draw a line and label it $\frac{1}{9}$.

➤ Using the unlabeled fraction section, draw a line to show $\frac{1}{24}$ and label it.

Compare. Write < or >.

$\frac{1}{12} \bigcirc \frac{1}{3}$ $\frac{1}{9} \bigcirc \frac{1}{6}$

$\frac{1}{24} \bigcirc \frac{1}{12}$ $\frac{1}{6} \bigcirc \frac{1}{24}$

Break Down the Box and More

Name_____

➤ Use your fraction squares to name and label each part of the unit square. Then draw smaller fraction pieces.

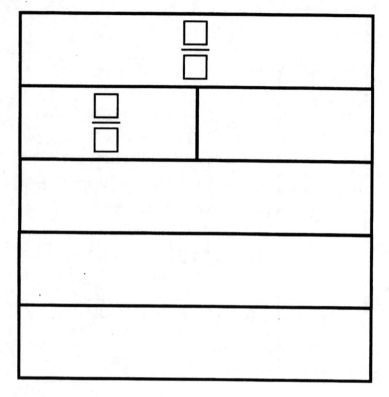

Compare. Write <, =, or >.

$\frac{1}{5}$ ◯ $\frac{1}{10}$ $\frac{2}{5}$ ◯ $\frac{4}{10}$

$\frac{3}{5}$ ◯ $\frac{7}{10}$ $\frac{4}{10}$ ◯ $\frac{4}{5}$

← Draw lines on this section to show $\frac{1}{20}$s. Label one of the sections.

← Draw lines on this section to show $\frac{1}{25}$s. Label one of the sections.

← Draw lines on this section to show $\frac{1}{100}$s. Label one of the sections.

Compare. Write < or >.

$\frac{1}{10}$ ◯ $\frac{1}{20}$ $\frac{1}{20}$ ◯ $\frac{1}{5}$ $\frac{1}{25}$ ◯ $\frac{1}{20}$ $\frac{1}{10}$ ◯ $\frac{1}{100}$

➤ Use the information above and what you learned on page 57 to compare the fraction pairs.

$\frac{1}{2}$ ◯ $\frac{1}{3}$ $\frac{1}{6}$ ◯ $\frac{1}{5}$ $\frac{1}{8}$ ◯ $\frac{1}{10}$ $\frac{1}{3}$ ◯ $\frac{1}{4}$

$\frac{1}{5}$ ◯ $\frac{1}{4}$ $\frac{1}{8}$ ◯ $\frac{1}{12}$ $\frac{1}{9}$ ◯ $\frac{1}{10}$ $\frac{1}{25}$ ◯ $\frac{1}{16}$

Find the Mixed Number

Name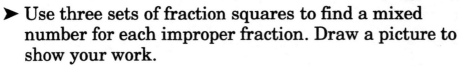

➤ Use three sets of fraction squares to find a mixed number for each improper fraction. Draw a picture to show your work.

$$\frac{5}{2} = \blacksquare\;\blacksquare\;\blacksquare = 2\frac{1}{2}$$

$$\mathbf{1} \;+\; \mathbf{1} \;+\; \frac{1}{2}$$

$\frac{8}{3} = \square\square\square = \underline{}$

$\frac{9}{4} = \square\square\square = \underline{}$

$\frac{17}{6} = \square\square\square = \underline{}$

$\frac{11}{8} = \square\square = \underline{}$

$\frac{13}{5} = \square\square\square = \underline{}$

$\frac{19}{10} = \square\square = \underline{}$

➤ Find the lowest-terms mixed number for each improper fraction.

$\frac{10}{4} = \square\square\square = \underline{} = \underline{}$

$\frac{12}{9} = \square\square = \underline{} = \underline{}$

$\frac{16}{6} = \square\square\square = \underline{} = \underline{}$

Add the Fractions: Common Denominators

Name_____

➤ Use your fraction squares on the unit square below to find each sum. Express your answers in lowest terms.

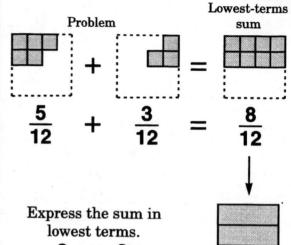

Problem

Lowest-terms sum

$$\frac{5}{12} + \frac{3}{12} = \frac{8}{12}$$

Express the sum in lowest terms.

$$\frac{8}{12} = \frac{2}{3}$$

Problem	Lowest-terms sum	Fraction picture		Problem	Lowest-terms sum	Fraction picture
$\frac{1}{5} + \frac{3}{5} =$	☐/☐	☐		$\frac{1}{4} + \frac{1}{4} =$	☐/☐	☐
$\frac{3}{6} + \frac{1}{6} =$	☐/☐	☐		$\frac{2}{12} + \frac{5}{12} =$	☐/☐	☐
$\frac{3}{8} + \frac{2}{8} =$	☐/☐	☐		$\frac{3}{10} + \frac{5}{10} =$	☐/☐	☐
$\frac{2}{6} + \frac{1}{6} =$	☐/☐	☐		$\frac{5}{12} + \frac{1}{12} =$	☐/☐	☐

Fractions in Action
© 1994 Learning Resources, Inc.

Add the Fractions: Unlike Denominators

Name_____

➤ Use your fraction squares on the unit square below to find each sum. Express your answers in lowest terms.

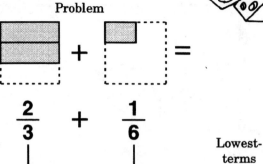

Problem

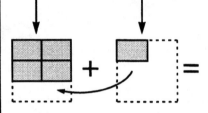

$$\frac{2}{3} + \frac{1}{6} =$$

Lowest-terms sum

$$\frac{4}{6} + \frac{1}{6} = \frac{5}{6}$$

Express fractions with common denominators.

Problem

$$\frac{1}{2} + \frac{1}{4}$$

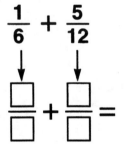

$$\frac{\Box}{\Box} + \frac{\Box}{\Box} =$$

Lowest-terms sum $\frac{\Box}{\Box}$

Fraction picture

Problem

$$\frac{1}{6} + \frac{5}{12}$$

$$\frac{\Box}{\Box} + \frac{\Box}{\Box} =$$

Lowest-terms sum $\frac{\Box}{\Box}$

Fraction picture

$$\frac{2}{5} + \frac{3}{10}$$

$$\frac{\Box}{\Box} + \frac{\Box}{\Box} =$$

Lowest-terms sum $\frac{\Box}{\Box}$

Fraction picture

$$\frac{1}{3} + \frac{5}{12}$$

$$\frac{\Box}{\Box} + \frac{\Box}{\Box} =$$

Lowest-terms sum $\frac{\Box}{\Box}$

Fraction picture

Sums Greater Than 1

Name_____

➤ Use two sets of fraction squares on the unit square below to find each sum. Express your answers as lowest-terms mixed numbers.

Problem

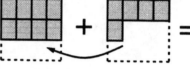

$$\frac{2}{3} + \frac{5}{12}$$

Express fractions with common denominators.

 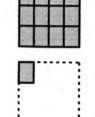

$$\frac{8}{12} + \frac{5}{12} =$$

$$= \frac{13}{12} = 1\frac{1}{12}$$

Problem

$$\frac{7}{8} + \frac{1}{4}$$

$$\frac{\square}{\square} + \frac{\square}{\square} = \frac{\square}{\square} =$$ _____

Fraction sum   Mixed number sum   Fraction picture

Problem

$$\frac{1}{2} + \frac{4}{5}$$

$$\frac{\square}{\square} + \frac{\square}{\square} = \frac{\square}{\square} =$$ _____

Fraction sum   Mixed number sum   Fraction picture

$$\frac{7}{10} + \frac{3}{5}$$

$$\frac{\square}{\square} + \frac{\square}{\square} = \frac{\square}{\square} =$$ _____

Fraction sum   Mixed number sum

$$\frac{2}{3} + \frac{5}{6}$$

$$\frac{\square}{\square} + \frac{\square}{\square} = \frac{\square}{\square} =$$ _____

Fraction sum   Mixed number sum

Fractions in Action
© 1994 Learning Resources, Inc.

Subtract with Common Denominators

Name_____

➤ Find each difference using your fraction squares on the unit square at the right. Draw a fraction picture to show your work.

Problem   Difference

$$\frac{5}{8} - \frac{2}{8} = \frac{3}{8}$$

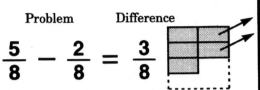

Problem   Difference   Fraction picture

$$\frac{3}{5} - \frac{1}{5} = \frac{\square}{\square}$$

$$\frac{7}{8} - \frac{4}{8} = \frac{\square}{\square}$$

$$\frac{7}{12} - \frac{2}{12} = \frac{\square}{\square}$$

Problem   Difference   Fraction picture

$$\frac{7}{10} - \frac{4}{10} = \frac{\square}{\square}$$

$$\frac{5}{6} - \frac{4}{6} = \frac{\square}{\square}$$

$$\frac{3}{4} - \frac{2}{4} = \frac{\square}{\square}$$

➤ Find each difference. Express your answers in lowest terms.

Problem	Difference	Lowest-terms difference	Fraction picture	Problem	Difference	Lowest-terms difference	Fraction picture
$\frac{3}{4} - \frac{1}{4} =$	$\frac{\square}{\square}$	$= \frac{\square}{\square}$		$\frac{7}{8} - \frac{1}{8} =$	$\frac{\square}{\square}$	$= \frac{\square}{\square}$	
$\frac{7}{10} - \frac{2}{10} =$	$\frac{\square}{\square}$	$= \frac{\square}{\square}$		$\frac{11}{12} - \frac{3}{12} =$	$\frac{\square}{\square}$	$= \frac{\square}{\square}$	

Subtract the Fractions: Unlike Denominators

Name_____

➤ Find each difference using your fraction squares on the unit square at the right. Draw a fraction picture to show your work.

$$\frac{5}{8} - \frac{1}{2}$$

$$\frac{5}{8} - \frac{4}{8} = \frac{1}{8}$$

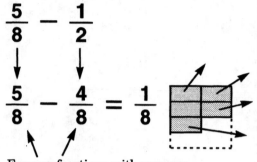

Express fractions with common denominators.

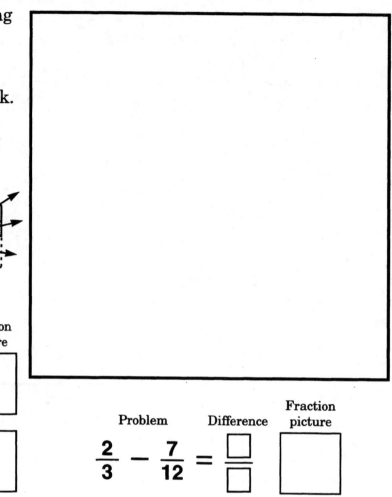

Problem	Difference	Fraction picture
$\frac{9}{12} - \frac{2}{3} =$	$\frac{\square}{\square}$	
$\frac{5}{6} - \frac{2}{3} =$	$\frac{\square}{\square}$	
$\frac{7}{10} - \frac{3}{5} =$	$\frac{\square}{\square}$	

Problem	Difference	Fraction picture
$\frac{2}{3} - \frac{7}{12} =$	$\frac{\square}{\square}$	
$\frac{1}{2} - \frac{1}{3} =$	$\frac{\square}{\square}$	

➤ Find each difference. Express your answers in lowest terms.

Problem	Difference	Lowest-terms difference	Fraction picture
$\frac{5}{6} - \frac{1}{2} =$	$\frac{\square}{\square}$	$= \frac{\square}{\square}$	
$\frac{3}{4} - \frac{5}{12} =$	$\frac{\square}{\square}$	$= \frac{\square}{\square}$	

Problem	Difference	Lowest-terms difference	Fraction picture
$\frac{5}{6} - \frac{4}{12} =$	$\frac{\square}{\square}$	$= \frac{\square}{\square}$	
$\frac{1}{2} - \frac{3}{10} =$	$\frac{\square}{\square}$	$= \frac{\square}{\square}$	

Multiply Fractions and Whole Numbers

Name_____

➤ Use three sets of fraction squares to multiply a fraction by a whole number. Draw a fraction picture to show your work.

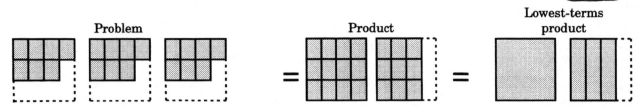

| Problem | Product | Lowest-terms product |

Meaning: Repeated addition

$$3 \times \frac{7}{12} = \left\{ \frac{7}{12} + \frac{7}{12} + \frac{7}{12} \right\} = \frac{21}{12} = 1\frac{9}{12} = 1\frac{3}{4}$$

Problem	Meaning: Repeated addition	Lowest-terms product	Fraction picture
$2 \times \frac{4}{5} =$		=	
$3 \times \frac{3}{4} =$		=	
$2 \times \frac{5}{6} =$		=	
$4 \times \frac{5}{12} =$		=	
$4 \times \frac{2}{3} =$		=	
$3 \times \frac{5}{6} =$		=	

Fractions in Action
© 1994 Learning Resources, Inc.

Multiply Fractions

Name_____

➤ Use your fraction squares to find each product. Draw a fraction picture to show your work.

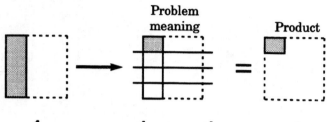

Problem meaning

Product

$\dfrac{1}{3}$

$\dfrac{1}{4}$ **of** $\dfrac{1}{3}$ = $\dfrac{1}{12}$

Here's another way to solve the problem: Make a cutout of $\dfrac{1}{3}$. Fold it in fourths. Now see how much $\dfrac{1}{4}$ is of $\dfrac{1}{3}$.

Problem	Meaning		Product	Fraction picture
$\dfrac{1}{2}$ of $\dfrac{3}{4}$		=	□/□	
$\dfrac{1}{3}$ of $\dfrac{1}{2}$		=	□/□	
$\dfrac{1}{2}$ of $\dfrac{5}{6}$		=	□/□	
$\dfrac{1}{4}$ of $\dfrac{8}{12}$		=	□/□	
$\dfrac{1}{3}$ of $\dfrac{9}{10}$		=	□/□	
$\dfrac{1}{4}$ of $\dfrac{4}{6}$		=	□/□	

Fractions in Action
© 1994 Learning Resources, Inc.

Dividing Fractions

Name_____

➤ Find each quotient using your fraction squares on the unit square at the right.

$$\frac{3}{4} \div \frac{1}{8}$$

means

How many $\frac{1}{8}$s can cover $\frac{3}{4}$?

$$\frac{3}{4} \div \frac{1}{8} = 6$$

It takes 6 of the $\frac{1}{8}$ pieces to cover $\frac{3}{4}$.

➤ Fill in the blanks. Then find the answer.

$1 \div \dfrac{1}{3}$ means: How many _____ can cover _____?   Answer: _____

$\dfrac{1}{2} \div \dfrac{1}{8}$ means: How many _____ can cover _____?   Answer: _____

$\dfrac{2}{3} \div \dfrac{1}{6}$ means: How many _____ can cover _____?   Answer: _____

$\dfrac{5}{6} \div \dfrac{1}{12}$ means: How many _____ can cover _____?   Answer: _____

$\dfrac{8}{10} \div \dfrac{2}{5}$ means: How many _____ can cover _____?   Answer: _____

Dividing Fractions Again

Name_____

➤ Find each quotient using your fraction squares on the unit square at the right.

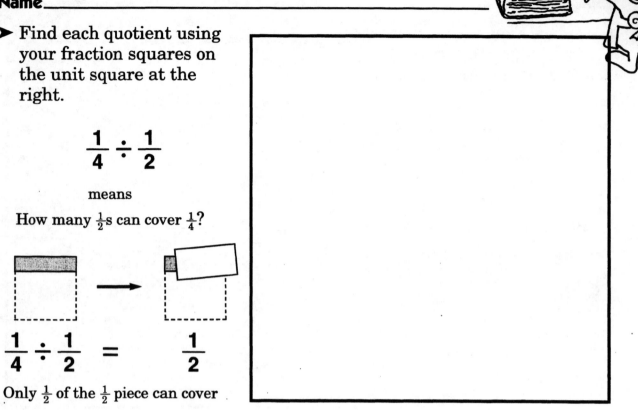

$$\frac{1}{4} \div \frac{1}{2}$$

means

How many $\frac{1}{2}$s can cover $\frac{1}{4}$?

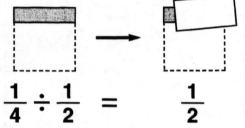

$$\frac{1}{4} \div \frac{1}{2} = \frac{1}{2}$$

Only $\frac{1}{2}$ of the $\frac{1}{2}$ piece can cover

➤ Fill in the blanks. Then find the answer.

$\frac{1}{2} \div \frac{1}{4}$ means: How many _____ can cover _____?   Answer: _____

$\frac{1}{2} \div \frac{1}{3}$ means: How many _____ can cover _____?   Answer: _____

$\frac{1}{2} \div \frac{3}{4}$ means: How many _____ can cover _____?   Answer: _____

$1 \div \frac{3}{4}$ means: How many _____ can cover _____?   Answer: _____

$\frac{5}{10} \div \frac{1}{2}$ means: How many _____ can cover _____?   Answer: _____

Fraction Squares: You've Got A Point

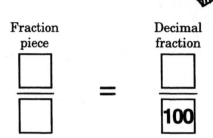

Name_____

➤ Use your fraction squares on the grid below to find a decimal equivalent to each given fraction.

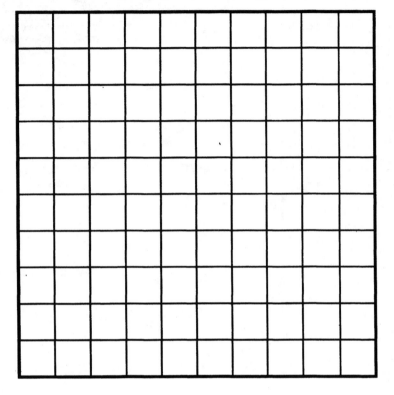

Fraction piece

$$\frac{\square}{\square} = \frac{\square}{100}$$

Decimal fraction

$$= \underline{\quad}\\ 0.\underline{\quad\quad}$$

Decimal

$\dfrac{1}{2} = \dfrac{\square}{100} = \underline{\quad}\\ 0.\underline{\quad}$

$\dfrac{1}{5} = \dfrac{\square}{100} = \underline{\quad\quad}$

$\dfrac{1}{3} = \dfrac{\square}{100} = \underline{\quad\quad}$

$\dfrac{1}{4} = \dfrac{\square}{100} = \underline{\quad\quad}$

$\dfrac{1}{10} = \dfrac{\square}{100} = \underline{\quad\quad}$

$\dfrac{1}{6} = \dfrac{\square}{100} = \underline{\quad\quad}$

$\dfrac{1}{8} = \dfrac{\square}{100} = \underline{\quad\quad}$

$1 = \dfrac{\square}{100} = \underline{\quad\quad}$

$\dfrac{1}{12} = \dfrac{\square}{100} = \underline{\quad\quad}$

Fraction Squares, Percent Parts

Name_____

➤ Use your fraction squares on the grid below to find a percent equivalent to each given fraction.

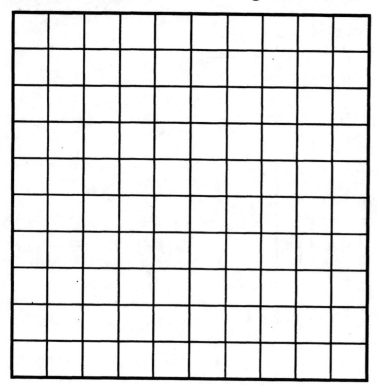

Fraction piece

$\dfrac{\Box}{\Box}$ =

Fraction "per 100"

$\dfrac{\Box}{100}$

=

_____%
Percent

$\dfrac{1}{2} = \dfrac{\Box}{100} = $ _____%

$\dfrac{1}{5} = \dfrac{\Box}{100} = $ _____%

$\dfrac{1}{3} = \dfrac{\Box}{100} = $ _____%

$\dfrac{1}{4} = \dfrac{\Box}{100} = $ _____%

$\dfrac{1}{10} = \dfrac{\Box}{100} = $ _____%

$\dfrac{1}{6} = \dfrac{\Box}{100} = $ _____%

$\dfrac{1}{8} = \dfrac{\Box}{100} = $ _____%

$1 = \dfrac{\Box}{100} = $ _____%

$\dfrac{1}{12} = \dfrac{\Box}{100} = $ _____%

Rainbow Fraction Tiles
Teaching Notes

Objectives

Use Rainbow Fraction Tiles:

- To model equivalent fractions and to compare fractions.
- To perform operations using fractions, whole numbers, and mixed numbers.
- To relate fractions to number lines and measurement.

Warm Up

In order for students to grasp the meaning of the fractional parts of a whole unit, have them fold, color, and label 8-inch strips of paper into halves, thirds, fourths, sixths, and eighths. Distribute colored pencils or crayons and six $8'' \times 1''$ strips of paper to each student and ask them to do the following:

1. Color one whole strip red and label it 1.
2. Fold one strip in half. Color each half pink and label it $\frac{1}{2}$.
3. Fold one strip in half, then in half again. Color each fourth yellow and label it $\frac{1}{4}$.
4. Fold one strip in half three times to yield eighths. Color each eighth blue and label it $\frac{1}{8}$.
5. Fold one strip into three equal parts. Color each third orange and label it $\frac{1}{3}$.
6. Fold one strip into thirds, then in half into sixths. Color each sixth teal and label it $\frac{1}{6}$.

Ask the students how they would show ninths or twelfths. Distribute more strips of paper to make ninths (brown), twelfths (black), fifths (green), and tenths (purple). Having students make their own sets of fraction tiles empowers them to make frac-

tion tiles for $\frac{1}{9}$s, $\frac{1}{15}$s, $\frac{1}{16}$s, $\frac{1}{18}$s, $\frac{1}{20}$s, or $\frac{1}{24}$s. They may encounter an addition or subtraction problem requiring a common denominator such as $\frac{1}{20}$ needed to find a particular sum or difference.

The 51 proportionally-sized fraction tiles are color-coded in nine colors to help students keep track of the fractional parts. Students can line up each color to make a fraction table from 1 through twelfths and then literally "see" sets of equivalent fractions (i.e., $\frac{1}{2} = \frac{2}{4}$ or $\frac{8}{12} = \frac{2}{3}$). A fraction tile table is shown on page 79.

Using a set of fraction tiles, ask students to line up the unit fractions, beginning with 1, halves, thirds, fourths, and so on through the twelfths.

Students should discover that the larger the denominator the smaller the unit-fraction piece.

1											
$\frac{1}{2}$						$\frac{1}{2}$					
$\frac{1}{3}$				$\frac{1}{3}$				$\frac{1}{3}$			
$\frac{1}{4}$			$\frac{1}{4}$			$\frac{1}{4}$			$\frac{1}{4}$		
$\frac{1}{5}$		$\frac{1}{5}$		$\frac{1}{5}$		$\frac{1}{5}$		$\frac{1}{5}$			
$\frac{1}{6}$		$\frac{1}{6}$		$\frac{1}{6}$		$\frac{1}{6}$		$\frac{1}{6}$		$\frac{1}{6}$	
$\frac{1}{8}$	$\frac{1}{8}$	$\frac{1}{8}$	$\frac{1}{8}$	$\frac{1}{8}$	$\frac{1}{8}$	$\frac{1}{8}$	$\frac{1}{8}$				
$\frac{1}{10}$	$\frac{1}{10}$	$\frac{1}{10}$	$\frac{1}{10}$	$\frac{1}{10}$	$\frac{1}{10}$	$\frac{1}{10}$	$\frac{1}{10}$	$\frac{1}{10}$	$\frac{1}{10}$		
$\frac{1}{12}$	$\frac{1}{12}$	$\frac{1}{12}$	$\frac{1}{12}$	$\frac{1}{12}$	$\frac{1}{12}$	$\frac{1}{12}$	$\frac{1}{12}$	$\frac{1}{12}$	$\frac{1}{12}$	$\frac{1}{12}$	$\frac{1}{12}$

Rainbow Fraction Tile Materials

Rainbow Fraction Tiles (LER 615)
Overhead Rainbow Fraction Tiles
  (LER 616)
Blackline masters on pages 75–77

 ## Using the Activity Pages

Equivalent Fractions *(page 78)*

Students are to find a lowest-terms equivalent fraction that will cover the same fraction-tile area as those shown. For example, six-eighths ($\frac{6}{8}$) can be covered exactly by three-fourths ($\frac{3}{4}$) to show $\frac{6}{8} = \frac{3}{4}$.

Comparing Fractions *(page 79)*

Two unit fraction tile outlines and a fraction table help students compare fractions. Direct students to show the two fractions of each problem on the unit fraction tile outlines, aligning the left sides as the starting point. They can see which fraction is larger than the other. Use the fraction tile fraction table to find and discuss sets of equivalent fractions.

Improper Fractions to Mixed Numbers *(page 80)*

Have groups of four students work cooperatively since four sets of fraction tiles are needed. Have each student draw a fraction-tile picture of the mixed number as accurately as possible.

Finding Common Denominators
(page 81)

Since two sets of fraction tiles are needed to find the common denominator (same-color tiles), have students work in pairs on this activity. Help students find the common denominator for the two fractions shown. Have them put two orange fraction tiles ($\frac{2}{3}$) on the top and three yellow fraction tiles ($\frac{3}{4}$) on the bottom. Students must find a same-color fraction tile that can cover both the orange tiles ($\frac{2}{3}$) and three yellow fraction tiles ($\frac{3}{4}$). After some experimentation with smaller same-color tiles such as $\frac{1}{8}$s (blue), $\frac{1}{10}$s (purple), and $\frac{1}{12}$s (black), students discover the black tiles ($\frac{1}{12}$s) can cover each of the two fractions exactly, showing $\frac{2}{3} = \frac{8}{12}$ and $\frac{3}{4} = \frac{9}{12}$. Direct the students to use the two unit fraction tiles at the top as a workspace for the four problems at the bottom.

Adding Fractions *(pages 82–83)*

Make an overhead transparency of page 82. Show a few addition examples with common denominators, and then move on to fractions with unlike denominators. You can refer back to page 81 and ask students how many black fraction tiles ($\frac{1}{12}$s) there are in all for the fractions $\frac{2}{3}$ and $\frac{3}{4}$.

Using all black tiles, $\frac{8}{12} + \frac{9}{12}$ will cover one unit fraction tile ($\frac{12}{12}$) and have $\frac{5}{12}$ covering the second unit fraction tile to show a sum of $1\frac{5}{12}$, or $\frac{8}{12} + \frac{9}{12} = \frac{17}{12} = \frac{12}{12} + \frac{5}{12} = 1\frac{5}{12}$.

Have students find the sums for each of the four problems at the bottom of page 81. [Answers: $\frac{5}{8}$, $\frac{7}{12}$, $\frac{9}{10}$, and $1\frac{7}{12}$.] Have students use pages 82 and 83 together to add fractions. Use page 82 as a workspace for the addition problems on page 83. Students need two sets of fraction tiles to complete page 83. Monitor students as they are working and ask them to explain how they are finding the sums.

Note: The processes for adding, subtracting, multiplying, and dividing fractions is the same whether the students are using fraction circles, squares, or tiles. Refer to the explanations found in the Teaching Notes, pages 7–11.

Subtracting Fractions (pages 84–85)

Make a transparency of page 84 to demonstrate how fractions can be subtracted from fractions or mixed numbers using tiles. Have students use pages 84 and 85 to subtract fractional numbers. Use page 84 as a workspace for the problems on page 85. Students will need two sets of fraction tiles for this activity.

Multiplying Fractions (pages 86–87)

Using pages 86 and 87, students will multiply a fraction by a whole number and a fraction by another fraction. To multiply a fraction by a whole number, try examples such as $5 \times \frac{1}{3}$ ["5 times $\frac{1}{3}$" $= \frac{5}{3} = 1\frac{2}{3}$] and $2 \times \frac{3}{4}$ ["2 times $\frac{3}{4}$" $= \frac{6}{4} = 1\frac{2}{4} = 1\frac{1}{2}$].

To multiply a fraction by another fraction, try examples $\frac{1}{2} \times \frac{4}{5}$ ["$\frac{1}{2}$ of $\frac{4}{5}$" $= \frac{2}{5}$] and $\frac{3}{4} \times \frac{2}{3}$ ["$\frac{3}{4}$ of $\frac{2}{3}$" = think: $\frac{3}{4}$ of $\frac{4}{6}$ is $\frac{3}{6}$ so $\frac{3}{4}$ of $\frac{2}{3} = \frac{3}{6} = \frac{1}{2}$]. Have students read each multiplication problem and tell what it means before they start with the fraction tiles.

Expressing the fraction to be multiplied as a larger equivalent fraction can enable students to understand the "parts" of the fraction entity, such as changing $\frac{3}{4} \times \frac{2}{3}$ to $\frac{3}{4} \times \frac{4}{6}$ above. Remember that a whole number may be expressed as $\frac{n}{1}$; for example, $2 \times \frac{3}{4} = \frac{2}{1} \times \frac{3}{4}$.

Dividing Fractions (pages 88–89)

The fraction tiles are especially appropriate for showing how to divide with fractional numbers. Students must remember the basic concept of division. For $3 \div \frac{1}{4}$, ask "How many $\frac{1}{4}$s are there in 3?" [12] For $\frac{2}{3} \div \frac{1}{6}$, ask "How many $\frac{1}{6}$s in $\frac{2}{3}$?" [4]

The situation changes with the problem $\frac{1}{2} \div \frac{3}{4}$ in that $\frac{1}{2}$ is a smaller fraction being divided by a larger fraction. The quotient will be less than 1.

Students may wish to change both fractions to have common denominators to see that $\frac{6}{12} \div \frac{9}{12}$ will show that only 6 of the 9 twelfths, or $\frac{2}{3}$ of $\frac{9}{12}$ covers $\frac{1}{2}$.

Fraction Connection to Number Lines *(page 90)*

The fraction tiles also can be used to bridge the gap between fraction manipulatives and number lines. Although number lines are a graphic way to show various concepts, some students find them to be quite abstract. Many students do not truly understand how the increments, especially on fraction number lines and inch rulers, are determined.

Make a transparency of the double-arrowed 0 to 1 number lines shown on page 77. Use it with the overhead fraction tiles to show number lines with various fractional increments.

Fraction Connection to Measurement *(page 91)*

Extend the construction of the number line to make a Giant Four-Inch Ruler focusing on 1, $\frac{1}{2}$, $\frac{1}{4}$, $\frac{1}{8}$, $\frac{1}{16}$ (and perhaps $\frac{1}{32}$) increments. Have them label the fraction parts on the ruler or draw the marks of varying lengths as shown on a standard inch ruler (very short marks for the $\frac{1}{16}$s, short marks for $\frac{1}{8}$s, and so on).

Provide tape or glue to attach the four pieces to make the giant ruler. Have students measure various objects in the classroom. Have them explain how to find measurements to the nearest $\frac{1}{16}$ of an "inch." Ask them how the measurements taken with this ruler differ from the measurements taken with a standard ruler or yardstick. [All measurements are 8 times smaller since this ruler has a ratio of 8:1 to a standard inch ruler].

Wrap Up

Performance evaluation. Ask students to compare fractions with unlike denominators using the fraction tiles. Since the Rainbow Fraction Tiles can be used very effectively to help students understand division of fractions, ask older students to show how to divide a fraction, whole number, or mixed number by a fraction using the fraction tiles.

Written assessment. Have students make a poster showing a picture of a fraction table made of fraction tiles, and a written explanation to find equivalent fractions. Ask older students to extend their thinking about the fraction tiles to make the connection to drawing and labeling number lines. Ask them to show an addition problem using fraction tiles to find its sum.

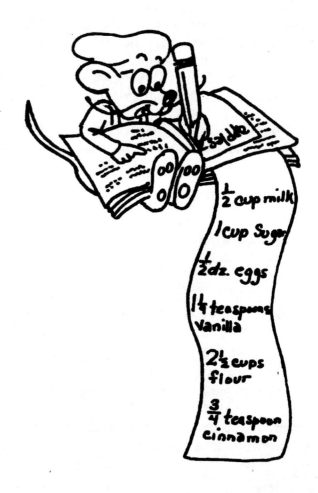

Fraction Tiles

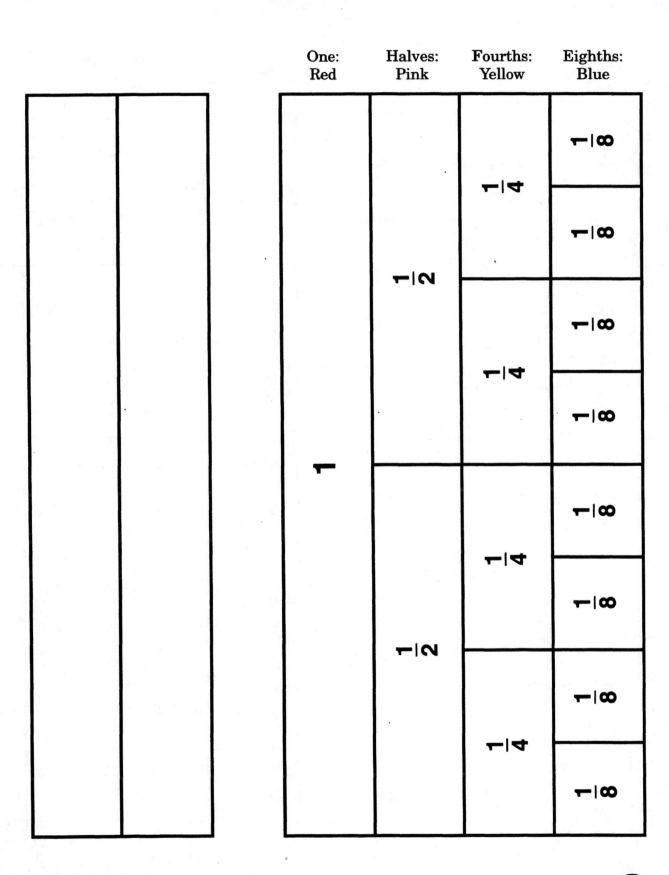

Fraction Tiles

Fifths: Green	Tenths: Purple
	$\frac{1}{10}$
$\frac{1}{5}$	
	$\frac{1}{10}$
	$\frac{1}{10}$
$\frac{1}{5}$	
	$\frac{1}{10}$
	$\frac{1}{10}$
$\frac{1}{5}$	
	$\frac{1}{10}$
	$\frac{1}{10}$
$\frac{1}{5}$	
	$\frac{1}{10}$
	$\frac{1}{10}$
$\frac{1}{5}$	
	$\frac{1}{10}$

One: Red	Thirds: Orange	Sixths: Teal	Twelfths: Black
			$\frac{1}{12}$
	$\frac{1}{3}$	$\frac{1}{6}$	$\frac{1}{12}$
			$\frac{1}{12}$
		$\frac{1}{6}$	$\frac{1}{12}$
1			$\frac{1}{12}$
	$\frac{1}{3}$	$\frac{1}{6}$	$\frac{1}{12}$
			$\frac{1}{12}$
		$\frac{1}{6}$	$\frac{1}{12}$
			$\frac{1}{12}$
	$\frac{1}{3}$	$\frac{1}{6}$	$\frac{1}{12}$
			$\frac{1}{12}$
		$\frac{1}{6}$	$\frac{1}{12}$

Fractions in Action
© 1994 Learning Resources, Inc.

Fraction Tiles

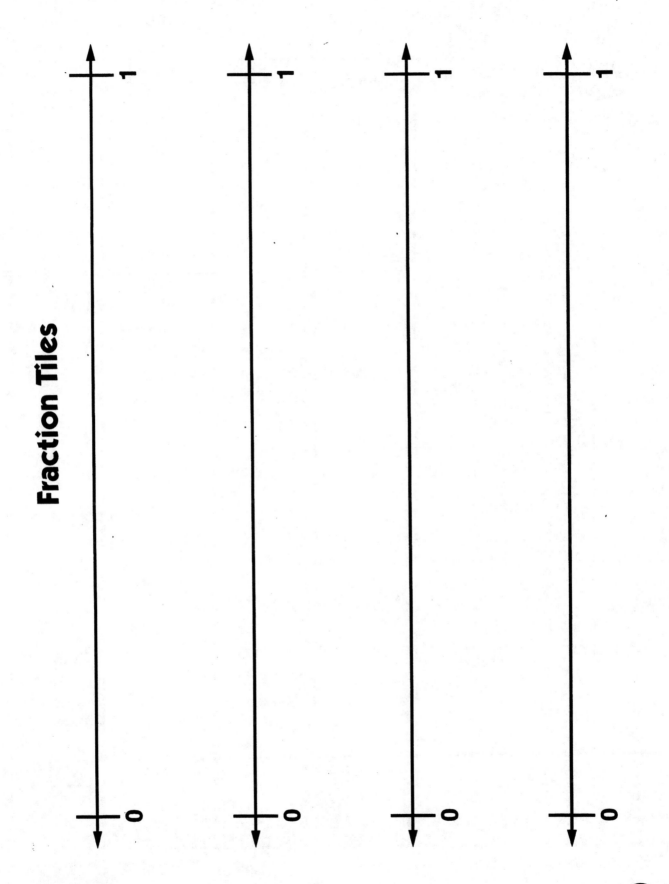

Name the Fraction

Name _____

▶ Cover each figure with fraction tiles, and name the fraction. Then cover each figure with the fewest number of fraction tiles to find the lowest-terms equivalent fraction.

Fraction ☐☐ = ☐☐ ☐☐ = ☐☐ ☐☐ = ☐☐ ☐☐ = ☐☐ ☐☐ = ☐☐ Lowest-terms fraction

Fractions in Action
© 1994 Learning Resources, Inc.

Compare the Pairs

Name _____

▶ Use your fraction tiles and the fraction table below to help you compare the fractions.

Show the first fraction here.→

Show the second fraction here.→

Write <, =, or >.

$\frac{1}{2} \bigcirc \frac{4}{6}$ $\frac{3}{8} \bigcirc \frac{1}{4}$ $\frac{3}{5} \bigcirc \frac{3}{4}$ $\frac{5}{6} \bigcirc \frac{5}{10}$

$\frac{2}{3} \bigcirc \frac{8}{12}$ $\frac{2}{3} \bigcirc \frac{3}{4}$ $\frac{5}{8} \bigcirc \frac{5}{6}$ $\frac{4}{6} \bigcirc \frac{8}{12}$

Fraction Table

Find the Mixed Number

Name_____

➤ On your desk, use four sets of fraction tiles to find a mixed number for each improper fraction.

➤ Shade the tiles below.

$\dfrac{10}{3}$ = 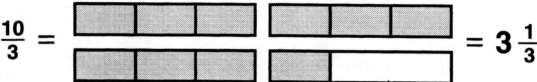 = $3\dfrac{1}{3}$

Fraction Tile Picture

$\dfrac{7}{4}$ = [ ] [ ] = ____

$\dfrac{25}{8}$ = [ ] [ ] = ____

$\dfrac{14}{3}$ = [ ] [ ] = ____

➤ Find the lowest-terms mixed number for each improper fraction. Draw a picture of your work.

$\dfrac{10}{4}$ = [ ] [ ] = ____ = ____

$\dfrac{20}{6}$ = [ ] [ ] = ____ = ____

$\dfrac{14}{4}$ = [ ] [ ] = ____ = ____

What Do We Have In Common?

Name _____

▶ Use two sets of fraction tiles for this activity.

Same denominator!

	Fraction		Fraction with common denominator

Show the first fraction here.→ $\dfrac{2}{3}$ = □/□

Show the second fraction here.→ $\dfrac{3}{4}$ = □/□

▶ Find equivalent fractions with common denominators for each pair of fractions.
① Use your fraction tiles to show each of the fractions in the pair.
② Then find smaller same-color fraction tiles to find the common denominator.

$\dfrac{1}{4}$ and $\dfrac{3}{8}$ → □/□ and □/□

$\dfrac{1}{3}$ and $\dfrac{1}{4}$ → □/□ and □/□

$\dfrac{2}{5}$ and $\dfrac{1}{2}$ → □/□ and □/□

$\dfrac{3}{4}$ and $\dfrac{5}{6}$ → □/□ and □/□

Fractions in Action
© 1994 Learning Resources, Inc.

81

Find the Sum

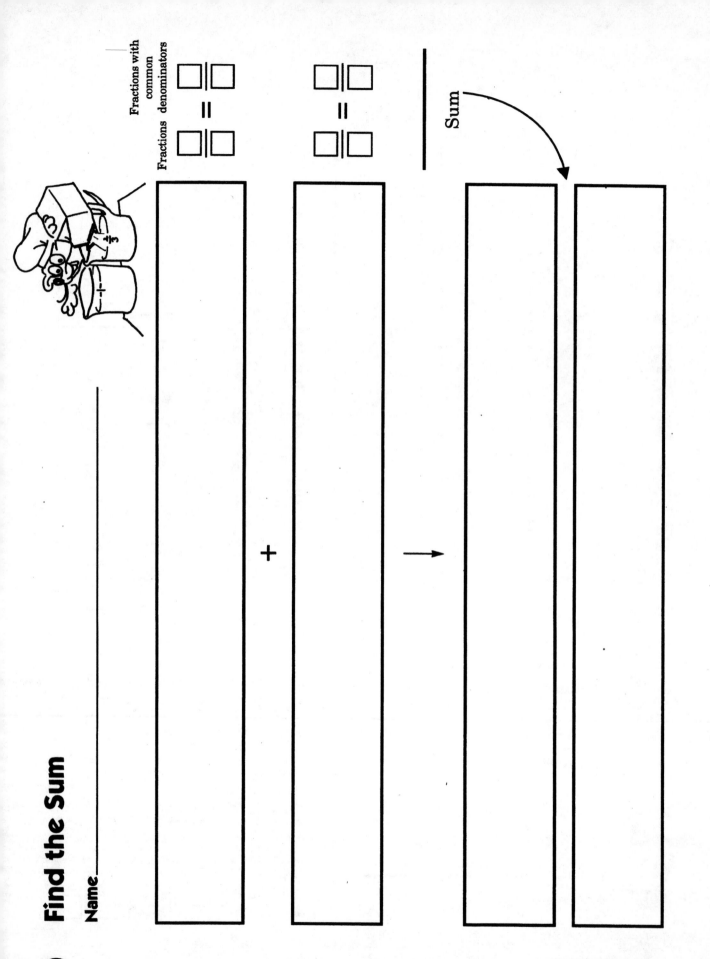

Fractions with common denominators

Fractions denominators

$$\square \square = \square \square$$

$$\square \square = \square \square$$

Sum

\+ →

Fractions in Action
© 1994 Learning Resources, Inc.

Sum it Up!

Name_____

➤ Use page 82 and two sets of fraction tiles to find each sum.
Express your answers in lowest terms.

$\frac{1}{2} = \frac{\square}{\square}$

$+ \ \frac{3}{8} = \frac{\square}{\square}$

_____

$\frac{5}{12} = \frac{\square}{\square}$

$+ \ \frac{1}{3} = \frac{\square}{\square}$

_____

$\frac{7}{10} = \frac{\square}{\square}$

$+ \ \frac{3}{5} = \frac{\square}{\square}$

_____

$\frac{4}{5} = \frac{\square}{\square}$

$+ \ \frac{1}{2} = \frac{\square}{\square}$

_____

$\frac{2}{3} = \frac{\square}{\square}$

$+ \ \frac{1}{4} = \frac{\square}{\square}$

_____

$\frac{5}{6} = \frac{\square}{\square}$

$+ \ \frac{3}{4} = \frac{\square}{\square}$

_____

$\frac{9}{10} = \frac{\square}{\square}$

$+ \ \frac{1}{2} = \frac{\square}{\square}$

_____

$\frac{5}{6} = \frac{\square}{\square}$

$+ \ \frac{2}{3} = \frac{\square}{\square}$

_____

$\frac{5}{12} = \frac{\square}{\square}$

$+ \ \frac{3}{4} = \frac{\square}{\square}$

_____

Find the Difference

Name _____

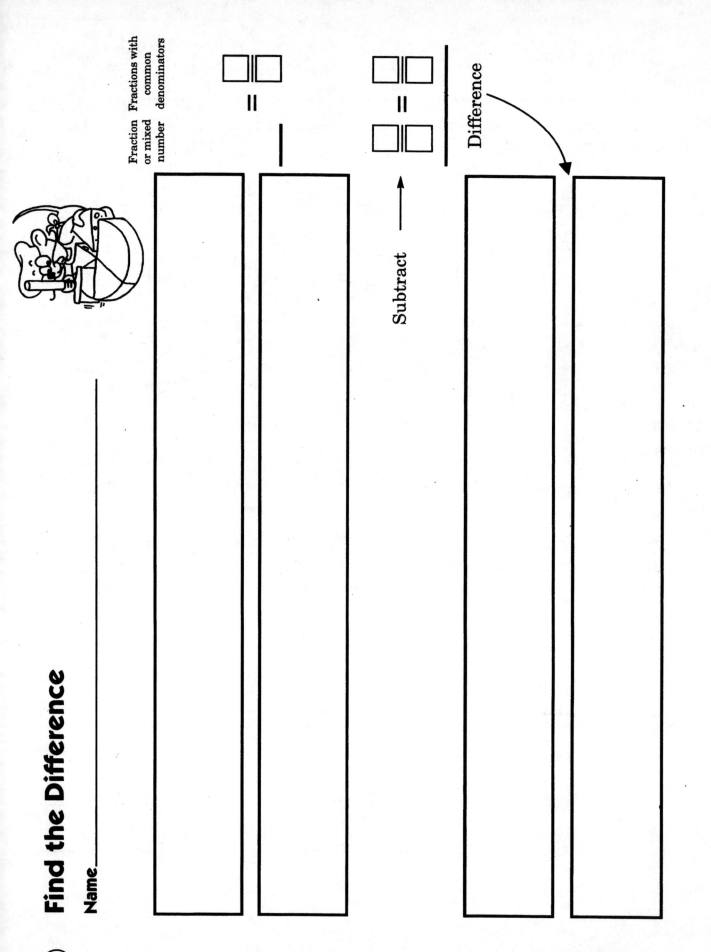

Fraction or mixed number

Fractions with common denominators

☐/☐ = ☐/☐

☐/☐ = ☐/☐

Subtract ⟶

Difference

Fractions in Action
© 1994 Learning Resources, Inc.

Find More Differences

Name_____

➤ Use page 84 and two sets of fraction tiles to find each difference. Express your answers in lowest terms.

$$\frac{7}{8} = \frac{\square}{\square}$$
$$-\frac{1}{2} = \frac{\square}{\square}$$
_____

$$\frac{2}{3} = \frac{\square}{\square}$$
$$-\frac{5}{12} = \frac{\square}{\square}$$
_____

$$\frac{1}{2} = \frac{\square}{\square}$$
$$-\frac{3}{10} = \frac{\square}{\square}$$
_____

$$1\frac{2}{3} = 1\frac{\square}{\square}$$
$$-\ \ \frac{1}{4} = \ \frac{\square}{\square}$$
_____

$$1\frac{1}{2} = \frac{\square}{\square}$$
$$-\ \ \frac{3}{4} = \frac{\square}{\square}$$
_____

$$\frac{3}{4} = \frac{\square}{\square}$$
$$-\frac{5}{12} = \frac{\square}{\square}$$
_____

$$1\frac{1}{10} = \frac{\square}{\square}$$
$$-\ \ \frac{3}{5} = \frac{\square}{\square}$$
_____

$$\frac{5}{6} = \frac{\square}{\square}$$
$$-\frac{3}{4} = \frac{\square}{\square}$$
_____

$$1\frac{5}{8} = \frac{\square}{\square}$$
$$-\ \ \frac{3}{4} = \frac{\square}{\square}$$
_____

Multiplying Fractions

Name _____

Ah! Ha!
½ of ¾ = ...

$$\frac{\square}{\square} \times \frac{\square}{\square} = \frac{\square}{\square}$$

More Multiplying Fractions

➤ Use three sets of fraction tiles and page 86 to help you multiply fractions and whole numbers. Express each product in lowest terms.

Meaning

Problem   Product   Mixed number product

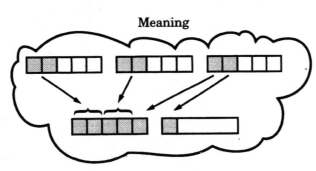

$$3 \times \frac{2}{5} = \qquad = \frac{6}{5} \qquad = 1\frac{1}{5}$$

$$4 \times \frac{1}{3} = \underline{\quad}$$

$$3 \times \frac{3}{4} = \underline{\quad}$$

$$2 \times \frac{3}{8} = \underline{\quad}$$

$$5 \times \frac{3}{10} = \underline{\quad}$$

$$3 \times \frac{5}{6} = \underline{\quad}$$

$$3 \times \frac{2}{5} = \underline{\quad}$$

Meaning

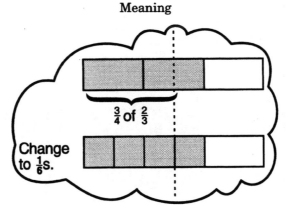

Problem   Product   Lowest-terms product

$$\frac{3}{4} \times \frac{2}{3} = \qquad = \frac{3}{6} \qquad = \frac{1}{2}$$

$$\frac{1}{3} \times \frac{3}{4} = \underline{\quad}$$

$$\frac{1}{2} \times \frac{3}{4} = \underline{\quad}$$

$$\frac{1}{4} \times \frac{2}{5} = \underline{\quad}$$

$$\frac{2}{3} \times \frac{9}{12} = \underline{\quad}$$

$$\frac{3}{4} \times \frac{1}{2} = \underline{\quad}$$

$$\frac{2}{3} \times \frac{6}{10} = \underline{\quad}$$

Dividing Fractions

Name _____

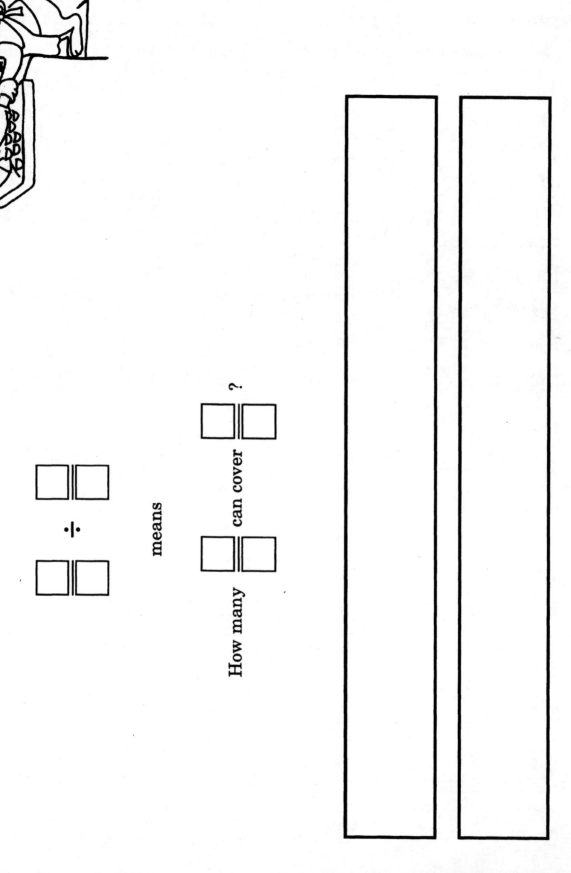

□□ ÷ □□

means

How many □□ can cover □□ ?

Fractions in Action
© 1994 Learning Resources, Inc.

More Dividing Fractions

Name _____

➤ Use your fraction tiles on the unit fraction tile at the right to find the solution to each division problem. Draw a picture to show your work.

Quotient   Fraction picture

How many $\dfrac{1}{4}$s in $\dfrac{1}{2}$?   ____

$$\dfrac{1}{2} \div \dfrac{1}{4} = \underline{\quad}$$

How many $\dfrac{1}{12}$s in $\dfrac{1}{3}$?   ____

$$\dfrac{1}{3} \div \dfrac{1}{12} = \underline{\quad}$$

How many $\dfrac{1}{6}$s in $\dfrac{2}{3}$?   ____

$$\dfrac{2}{3} \div \dfrac{1}{6} = \underline{\quad}$$

How many $\dfrac{1}{5}$s in $\dfrac{8}{10}$?   ____

$$\dfrac{8}{10} \div \dfrac{1}{5} = \underline{\quad}$$

How many $\dfrac{1}{3}$s in 1 ?   ____

$$1 \div \dfrac{1}{3} = \underline{\quad}$$

How many $\dfrac{2}{5}$s in $\dfrac{8}{10}$?   ____

$$\dfrac{8}{10} \div \dfrac{2}{5} = \underline{\quad}$$

How many $\dfrac{1}{2}$s in $\dfrac{1}{4}$?   ____

$$\dfrac{1}{4} \div \dfrac{1}{2} = \underline{\quad}$$

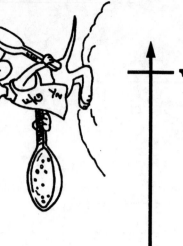

Get In Line With Fractions

Name _____

➤ Use your fraction tiles for each of the fractions below and mark increments on each number line.

$\frac{1}{8}$'s

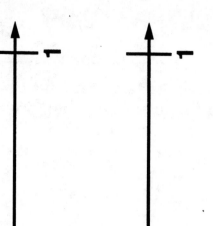

0 ⟶ 1

$\frac{1}{10}$'s

0 ⟶ 1

$\frac{1}{12}$'s

0 ⟶ 1

$\frac{1}{9}$'s

0 ⟶ 1

Fractions in Action
© 1994 Learning Resources, Inc.

Measure Up with Fractions

Name

▶ Use your fraction tiles to make a Giant Four-Inch Ruler with fraction marks for $\frac{1}{2}$, $\frac{1}{4}$, $\frac{1}{8}$, and $\frac{1}{16}$. Tape or glue the ruler pieces together to make a long ruler. Then use this ruler to measure objects in the classroom.

Fractions in Action
© 1994 Learning Resources, Inc.

Solutions

Page 16: $\frac{2}{2}$, $\frac{3}{3}$, $\frac{4}{4}$, $\frac{5}{5}$, $\frac{6}{6}$, $\frac{8}{8}$, $\frac{10}{10}$, $\frac{12}{12}$; $1=\frac{2}{2}=\frac{3}{3}=\frac{4}{4}=\frac{5}{5}=\frac{6}{6}=\frac{8}{8}=\frac{10}{10}=\frac{12}{12}$, $1=\frac{9}{9}=\frac{15}{15}=\frac{16}{16}=\frac{20}{20}=\frac{24}{24}=\frac{25}{25}=\frac{50}{50}=\frac{100}{100}$

Page 17: $\frac{1}{2}$: $\frac{1}{2}$, $\frac{2}{4}$, $\frac{3}{6}$, $\frac{4}{8}$, $\frac{5}{10}$, $\frac{6}{12}$. $\frac{1}{4}$: $\frac{1}{4}$, $\frac{2}{8}$, $\frac{3}{12}$. $\frac{1}{3}$: $\frac{1}{3}$, $\frac{2}{6}$, $\frac{4}{12}$

Page 18: $1=\frac{2}{2}=\frac{3}{3}=\frac{4}{4}=\frac{5}{5}=\frac{6}{6}=\frac{8}{8}=\frac{10}{10}=\frac{12}{12}$. $\frac{1}{2}=\frac{2}{4}=\frac{3}{6}=\frac{4}{8}=\frac{5}{10}=\frac{6}{12}$, $\frac{1}{3}=\frac{2}{6}=\frac{4}{12}$

Page 19: column 1: $\frac{4}{8}=\frac{1}{2}$, $\frac{4}{6}=\frac{2}{3}$, $\frac{5}{10}=\frac{1}{2}$, $\frac{4}{12}=\frac{1}{3}$; column 2: $\frac{6}{12}=\frac{1}{2}$, $\frac{8}{12}=\frac{2}{3}$, $\frac{8}{10}=\frac{4}{5}$, $\frac{9}{12}=\frac{3}{4}$ Note: for all fraction pictures, check students' drawings to match process and solution.

Page 20: top row: $\frac{1}{2}$, $\frac{1}{3}$; middle row: $\frac{1}{4}$, $\frac{1}{5}$, $\frac{1}{6}$; bottom row: $\frac{1}{8}$, $\frac{1}{10}$, $\frac{1}{12}$; rainbow: black, purple, blue, teal, green, yellow, orange, pink fraction pieces; rainbow fractions: $\frac{1}{12}$, –, $\frac{1}{8}$, $\frac{1}{6}$, $\frac{1}{5}$, –, $\frac{1}{3}$, –

Page 21: rainbow fractions: $\frac{1}{12}$, $\frac{1}{10}$, $\frac{1}{8}$, $\frac{1}{6}$, $\frac{1}{5}$, $\frac{1}{4}$, $\frac{1}{3}$, –; $\frac{1}{12}<\frac{1}{10}<\frac{1}{8}<\frac{1}{6}<\frac{1}{5}<\frac{1}{4}<\frac{1}{3}<\frac{1}{2}$; $\frac{1}{2}>\frac{1}{3}>\frac{1}{4}>\frac{1}{5}>\frac{1}{6}>\frac{1}{8}>\frac{1}{10}>\frac{1}{12}$; row 1: $\frac{1}{6}<\frac{1}{3}$, $\frac{1}{2}>\frac{1}{4}$, $\frac{1}{8}<\frac{1}{4}$, $\frac{1}{5}<\frac{1}{4}$; row 2: $\frac{1}{3}>\frac{1}{12}$, $\frac{1}{10}>\frac{1}{12}$, $\frac{1}{2}>\frac{1}{6}$, $\frac{1}{8}>\frac{1}{10}$

Page 22: larger than $\frac{2}{3}$: $\frac{7}{10}$, $\frac{3}{4}$, $\frac{4}{5}$, $\frac{5}{6}$, $\frac{7}{8}$, $\frac{9}{10}$, $\frac{11}{12}$. less than $\frac{1}{2}$: $\frac{1}{12}$, $\frac{1}{10}$, $\frac{1}{8}$, $\frac{1}{6}$, $\frac{1}{5}$, $\frac{1}{4}$, $\frac{3}{10}$, $\frac{1}{3}$, $\frac{3}{8}$, $\frac{2}{5}$, $\frac{5}{12}$

Page 23: row 1: $\frac{1}{2}=\frac{3}{6}$, $\frac{1}{3}>\frac{2}{12}$, $\frac{1}{4}<\frac{2}{5}$, $\frac{1}{6}<\frac{2}{3}$; row 2: $\frac{2}{5}>\frac{3}{10}$, $\frac{4}{6}=\frac{2}{3}$, $\frac{7}{10}<\frac{6}{8}$, $\frac{4}{5}>\frac{3}{4}$; row 3: $\frac{4}{12}=\frac{2}{6}$, $\frac{2}{8}=\frac{3}{12}$, $\frac{7}{8}>\frac{7}{12}$, $\frac{1}{3}<\frac{3}{8}$

Page 24: row 1: $\frac{4}{3}=1\frac{1}{3}$, $\frac{8}{5}=1\frac{3}{5}$, $\frac{7}{4}=1\frac{3}{4}$; row 2: $\frac{7}{6}=1\frac{1}{6}$, $\frac{13}{8}=1\frac{5}{8}$, $\frac{19}{12}=1\frac{7}{12}$; row 3: $\frac{6}{4}=1\frac{1}{2}$, $\frac{10}{8}=1\frac{1}{4}$, $\frac{9}{6}=1\frac{1}{2}$; row 4: $\frac{12}{10}=1\frac{1}{5}$, $\frac{15}{12}=1\frac{1}{4}$, $\frac{10}{6}=1\frac{2}{3}$

Page 25: column 1: $\frac{3}{4}$, $\frac{7}{8}$, $\frac{4}{5}$, $\frac{5}{6}$, $\frac{7}{10}$, $\frac{7}{12}$; column 2: $\frac{2}{4}=\frac{1}{2}$, $\frac{6}{8}=\frac{3}{4}$, $\frac{9}{12}=\frac{3}{4}$

Page 26: column 1: $1\frac{1}{3}$, $1\frac{2}{5}$, $1\frac{1}{4}$, $1\frac{5}{12}$; column 2: $1\frac{1}{2}$, $1\frac{1}{2}$, $1\frac{1}{3}$

Page 27: top: $\frac{1}{4}=\frac{3}{12}$ and $\frac{1}{6}=\frac{2}{12}$; bottom: $\frac{1}{3}=\frac{4}{12}$ and $\frac{1}{4}=\frac{3}{12}$

Page 28: $\frac{2}{4}+\frac{1}{4}=\frac{3}{4}$, $\frac{4}{6}+\frac{1}{6}=\frac{5}{6}$, $\frac{2}{8}+\frac{3}{8}=\frac{5}{8}$, $\frac{5}{10}+\frac{2}{10}=\frac{7}{10}$, $\frac{9}{12}+\frac{2}{12}=\frac{11}{12}$, $\frac{8}{12}+\frac{3}{12}=\frac{11}{12}$

Page 29: $\frac{3}{12}+\frac{3}{12}=\frac{6}{12}=\frac{1}{2}$, $\frac{1}{10}+\frac{4}{10}=\frac{5}{10}=\frac{1}{2}$, $\frac{8}{12}+\frac{2}{12}=\frac{10}{12}=\frac{5}{6}$, $\frac{3}{6}+\frac{1}{6}=\frac{4}{6}=\frac{2}{3}$, $\frac{1}{12}+\frac{8}{12}=\frac{9}{12}=\frac{3}{4}$, $\frac{1}{6}+\frac{2}{6}=\frac{3}{6}=\frac{1}{2}$

Page 30: $\frac{2}{8}+\frac{7}{8}=\frac{9}{8}=1\frac{1}{8}$, $\frac{5}{6}+\frac{2}{6}=\frac{7}{6}=1\frac{1}{6}$, $\frac{6}{10}+\frac{7}{10}=\frac{13}{10}=1\frac{3}{10}$, $\frac{2}{4}+\frac{3}{4}=\frac{5}{4}=1\frac{1}{4}$, $\frac{7}{12}+\frac{8}{12}=\frac{15}{12}=1\frac{1}{4}$, $\frac{6}{10}+\frac{9}{10}=\frac{15}{10}=1\frac{1}{2}$

Page 31: column 1: $\frac{2}{3}+\frac{1}{3}=1$, $\frac{2}{6}+\frac{2}{6}=1$, $\frac{2}{3}+\frac{4}{12}=1$, $\frac{1}{4}+\frac{3}{4}=1$, $\frac{3}{4}+\frac{2}{8}=1$, $\frac{3}{12}+\frac{3}{4}=1$, $\frac{1}{2}+\frac{2}{4}=1$, $\frac{1}{2}+\frac{1}{2}=1$, column 2: $\frac{5}{10}+\frac{1}{2}=1$, $\frac{1}{2}+\frac{3}{6}=1$, $\frac{4}{8}+\frac{1}{2}=1$

Page 32: column 1: $\frac{1}{6}$, $\frac{3}{8}$, $\frac{3}{5}$, $\frac{3}{10}$, $\frac{5}{12}$, $\frac{1}{8}$, $\frac{2}{5}$; column 2: $\frac{2}{4}=\frac{1}{2}$, $\frac{4}{6}=\frac{2}{3}$, $\frac{2}{12}=\frac{1}{6}$

Page 33: $\frac{4}{8}-\frac{3}{8}=\frac{1}{8}$, $\frac{5}{8}-\frac{2}{8}=\frac{3}{8}$, $\frac{8}{10}-\frac{7}{10}=\frac{1}{10}$, $\frac{8}{12}-\frac{5}{12}=\frac{3}{12}=\frac{1}{4}$, $\frac{5}{6}-\frac{3}{6}=\frac{2}{6}=\frac{1}{3}$, $\frac{8}{12}-\frac{5}{12}=\frac{3}{12}=\frac{1}{4}$

Page 34: $1\frac{6}{8}-\frac{3}{8}=1\frac{3}{8}$, $1\frac{5}{10}-\frac{4}{10}=1\frac{1}{10}$, $1\frac{6}{8}-\frac{5}{8}=1\frac{1}{8}$, $1\frac{8}{12}-\frac{5}{12}=1\frac{3}{12}=1\frac{1}{4}$, $1\frac{10}{12}-\frac{7}{12}=1\frac{3}{12}=1\frac{1}{4}$, $1\frac{8}{10}-\frac{5}{10}=1\frac{3}{10}$

Solutions

Page 35: $\frac{5}{4}-\frac{2}{4}=\frac{3}{4}$, $\frac{16}{10}-\frac{7}{10}=\frac{9}{10}$, $\frac{13}{8}-\frac{6}{8}=\frac{7}{8}$, $\frac{6}{6}-\frac{4}{6}=\frac{2}{6}=\frac{1}{3}$, $1\frac{8}{8}-\frac{5}{8}=1\frac{3}{8}$, $\frac{8}{6}-\frac{5}{6}=\frac{3}{6}=\frac{1}{2}$

Page 36: 5 of $\frac{1}{8}=\frac{5}{8}$, 3 of $\frac{1}{4}=\frac{3}{4}$, 4 of $\frac{1}{6}=\frac{4}{6}$ (or $\frac{2}{3}$), 9 of $\frac{1}{10}$ is $\frac{9}{10}$

Page 37: $4\times\frac{1}{5}=\frac{1}{5}+\frac{1}{5}+\frac{1}{5}+\frac{1}{5}=\frac{4}{5}$, $3\times\frac{2}{3}=\frac{2}{3}+\frac{2}{3}+\frac{2}{3}=\frac{6}{3}=2$, $3\times\frac{2}{5}=\frac{2}{5}+\frac{2}{5}+\frac{2}{5}=\frac{6}{5}=1\frac{1}{5}$, $4\times\frac{3}{8}=\frac{3}{8}+\frac{3}{8}+\frac{3}{8}+\frac{3}{8}=\frac{12}{8}=1\frac{4}{8}=1\frac{1}{2}$, $2\times\frac{5}{6}=\frac{5}{6}+\frac{5}{6}=\frac{10}{6}=1\frac{4}{6}=1\frac{2}{3}$, $5\times\frac{3}{10}=\frac{3}{10}+\frac{3}{10}+\frac{3}{10}+\frac{3}{10}+\frac{3}{10}=\frac{15}{10}=1\frac{5}{10}=1\frac{1}{2}$

Page 38: $\frac{1}{2}$ of $\frac{4}{5}=\frac{2}{5}$, $\frac{1}{3}$ of $\frac{1}{2}=\frac{1}{6}$, $\frac{1}{2}$ of $\frac{5}{6}=\frac{5}{12}$, $\frac{1}{2}$ of $\frac{2}{3}=\frac{1}{3}$, $\frac{1}{3}$ of $\frac{6}{10}=\frac{2}{10}=\frac{1}{5}$, $\frac{1}{4}$ of $\frac{2}{3}$ (think $\frac{1}{4}$ of $\frac{8}{12}$)$=\frac{2}{12}=\frac{1}{6}$

Page 39: How many $\frac{1}{2}$s can cover 1? 2;
How many $\frac{1}{4}$s can cover $\frac{3}{4}$? 3;
How many $\frac{1}{8}$s can cover $\frac{1}{2}$? 4;
How many $\frac{1}{10}$s can cover $\frac{4}{5}$? 8;
How many $\frac{1}{6}$s can cover $\frac{2}{3}$? 4

Page 40: How many $\frac{1}{4}$s can cover $\frac{1}{2}$? 2;
How many $\frac{1}{2}$s can cover $\frac{1}{4}$? $\frac{1}{2}$;
How many $\frac{1}{2}$s can cover $\frac{3}{4}$? $1\frac{1}{2}$;
How many $\frac{2}{3}$s can cover 1? $1\frac{1}{2}$;
How many $\frac{1}{3}$s can cover $\frac{5}{6}$? $2\frac{1}{2}$

Page 41: column 1: 15, 20, 10, 5, 6;
column 2: 45, 40, 24, 50, 55

Page 42: Dave's Day:

School	$\frac{1}{2}$ day	6 hours
Homework	$\frac{1}{4}$ day	3 hours
Meals	$\frac{1}{6}$ day	2 hours
Ride	$\frac{1}{12}$ day	1 hour

Simone's Saturday:

Shopping	4 hours	$\frac{1}{3}$ day
Eat lunch	1 hour	$\frac{1}{12}$ day
Movie	2 hours	$\frac{1}{6}$ day
Picnic	5 hours	$\frac{5}{12}$ day

Page 43: column 1: 180°, 120°, 60°, 30°, 36°;
column 2: 45°, 72°, 270°, 240°, 150°

Page 44: column 1: 50%, 25%, 10%, 75%, 30%;
column 2: 40%, $12\frac{1}{2}$%, $37\frac{1}{2}$%, $33\frac{1}{3}$%, $66\frac{2}{3}$%;
column 3: $16\frac{2}{3}$%, $83\frac{1}{3}$%, $8\frac{1}{3}$%, $41\frac{2}{3}$%, $58\frac{1}{3}$%

Page 45: Student Field Trip:

Grade 4 girls	$\frac{1}{4}$	25%	90°
Grade 5 girls	$\frac{1}{4}$	25%	90°
Grade 4 boys	$\frac{3}{8}$	$37\frac{1}{2}$%	135°
Grade 5 boys	$\frac{1}{8}$	$12\frac{1}{2}$%	45°

Favorite Class Survey:

Math	$\frac{1}{4}$	25%	90°
History	$\frac{3}{10}$	30%	108°
English	$\frac{1}{6}$	$16\frac{2}{3}$%	60°
Science	$\frac{1}{5}$	20%	72°
Other	$\frac{1}{12}$	$8\frac{1}{3}$%	30°

Page 46: Symphony Orchestra:

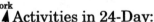

Strings	$\frac{1}{2}$	50%	180°
Woodwinds	$\frac{1}{4}$	25%	90°
Brass	$\frac{1}{6}$	$16\frac{2}{3}$%	60°
Percussion	$\frac{1}{12}$	$8\frac{1}{3}$%	30°

Activities in 24-Day:

Sleep	$\frac{1}{3}$	$33\frac{1}{3}$%	120°
Eat	$\frac{1}{12}$	$8\frac{1}{3}$%	30°
School	$\frac{1}{4}$	25%	90°
Homework	$\frac{1}{12}$	$8\frac{1}{3}$%	30°
Television	$\frac{1}{8}$	$12\frac{1}{2}$%	45°
Other	$\frac{1}{8}$	$12\frac{1}{2}$%	45°

Page 54: A: 1, B: $\frac{1}{4}$, C: $\frac{1}{2}$, D: $\frac{1}{3}$, E: $\frac{1}{6}$, F: $\frac{1}{12}$, G: $\frac{1}{8}$, H: $\frac{1}{10}$, I: $\frac{1}{5}$

Solutions

Page 55: $\frac{2}{2}$, $\frac{3}{3}$, $\frac{4}{4}$, $\frac{5}{5}$, $\frac{6}{6}$, $\frac{8}{8}$, $\frac{10}{10}$, $\frac{12}{12}$;
$1=\frac{2}{2}=\frac{3}{3}=\frac{4}{4}=\frac{5}{5}=\frac{6}{6}=\frac{8}{8}=\frac{10}{10}=\frac{12}{12}$;
$1=\frac{9}{9}=\frac{15}{15}=\frac{16}{16}=\frac{20}{20}=\frac{24}{24}=\frac{25}{25}=\frac{32}{32}=\frac{64}{64}$

Page 56: $\frac{1}{2}=\frac{6}{12}$; row 1: $\frac{1}{3}=\frac{2}{6}$, $\frac{1}{4}=\frac{3}{12}$, $\frac{2}{5}=\frac{4}{10}$, $\frac{8}{12}=\frac{2}{3}$;
row 2: $\frac{5}{10}=\frac{1}{2}$, $\frac{3}{4}=\frac{9}{12}$, $\frac{2}{6}=\frac{4}{12}$, $\frac{2}{3}=\frac{8}{12}$;
row 3: $\frac{1}{5}=\frac{2}{10}$, $\frac{6}{12}=\frac{4}{8}$,
$\frac{5}{6}=\frac{10}{12}$, $\frac{2}{8}=\frac{3}{12}$

Page 57: $\frac{1}{2}>\frac{1}{4}$, $\frac{1}{8}<\frac{1}{4}$,
$\frac{1}{8}>\frac{1}{16}$, $\frac{1}{32}<\frac{1}{16}$,
$\frac{1}{16}>\frac{1}{4}$, $\frac{1}{32}<\frac{1}{2}$

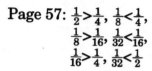

$\frac{1}{3}>\frac{1}{6}$, $\frac{1}{6}>\frac{1}{12}$,
$\frac{1}{12}<\frac{1}{3}$, $\frac{1}{9}<\frac{1}{6}$,
$\frac{1}{24}<\frac{1}{12}$, $\frac{1}{6}>\frac{1}{24}$

Page 58: $\frac{1}{5}>\frac{1}{10}$, $\frac{2}{5}=\frac{4}{10}$,
$\frac{3}{5}<\frac{7}{10}$, $\frac{4}{10}<\frac{4}{5}$
row 1: $\frac{1}{10}>\frac{1}{20}$, $\frac{1}{20}<\frac{1}{5}$, $\frac{1}{25}<\frac{1}{20}$, $\frac{1}{10}>\frac{1}{100}$
row 2: $\frac{1}{2}>\frac{1}{3}$, $\frac{1}{6}<\frac{1}{5}$, $\frac{1}{8}>\frac{1}{10}$, $\frac{1}{3}>\frac{1}{4}$
row 3: $\frac{1}{5}<\frac{1}{4}$, $\frac{1}{8}>\frac{1}{12}$, $\frac{1}{9}>\frac{1}{10}$, $\frac{1}{25}<\frac{1}{16}$

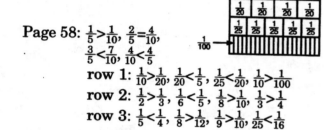

Page 59: top: $\frac{8}{3}=2\frac{2}{3}$, $\frac{9}{4}=2\frac{1}{4}$, $\frac{17}{6}=2\frac{5}{6}$, $\frac{11}{8}=1\frac{3}{8}$,
$\frac{13}{5}=2\frac{3}{5}$, $\frac{19}{10}=1\frac{9}{10}$;
bottom: $\frac{10}{4}=2\frac{2}{4}=2\frac{1}{2}$, $\frac{12}{9}=1\frac{3}{9}=1\frac{1}{3}$,
$\frac{16}{6}=2\frac{4}{6}=2\frac{2}{3}$

Page 60: column 1: $\frac{4}{5}$, $(\frac{4}{6})$ $\frac{2}{3}$, $\frac{5}{8}$, $(\frac{3}{6})$ $\frac{1}{2}$;
column 2: $(\frac{2}{4})$ $\frac{1}{2}$, $\frac{7}{12}$, $(\frac{8}{10})$ $\frac{4}{5}$, $(\frac{6}{12})$ $\frac{1}{2}$

Page 61: $\frac{2}{4}+\frac{1}{4}=\frac{3}{4}$, $\frac{2}{12}+\frac{5}{12}=\frac{7}{12}$,
$\frac{4}{10}+\frac{3}{10}=\frac{7}{10}$, $\frac{4}{12}+\frac{5}{12}=\frac{9}{12}=\frac{3}{4}$

Page 62: $\frac{7}{8}+\frac{2}{8}=\frac{9}{8}=1\frac{1}{8}$, $\frac{7}{10}+\frac{6}{10}=\frac{13}{10}=1\frac{3}{10}$,
$\frac{5}{10}+\frac{8}{10}=\frac{13}{10}=1\frac{3}{10}$, $\frac{4}{6}+\frac{5}{6}=\frac{9}{6}=1\frac{3}{6}=1\frac{1}{2}$

Page 63: top: $\frac{2}{5}$, $\frac{3}{8}$, $\frac{5}{12}$, $\frac{1}{6}$, $\frac{3}{10}$, $\frac{1}{4}$;
bottom: $\frac{2}{4}=\frac{1}{2}$, $\frac{6}{8}=\frac{3}{4}$, $\frac{5}{10}=\frac{1}{2}$ $\frac{8}{12}=\frac{2}{3}$

Page 64: top: $\frac{1}{12}$, $\frac{1}{6}$, $\frac{1}{10}$, $\frac{1}{12}$, $\frac{1}{6}$;
bottom: $\frac{2}{6}=\frac{1}{3}$, $\frac{6}{12}=\frac{1}{2}$, $\frac{4}{12}=\frac{1}{3}$ $\frac{2}{10}=\frac{1}{5}$

Page 65: $2\times\frac{4}{5}=\frac{4}{5}+\frac{4}{5}=\frac{8}{5}=1\frac{3}{5}$,
$3\times\frac{3}{4}=\frac{3}{4}+\frac{3}{4}+\frac{3}{4}=\frac{9}{4}=2\frac{1}{4}$,
$2\times\frac{5}{6}=\frac{5}{6}+\frac{5}{6}=\frac{10}{6}=(1\frac{4}{6})\ 1\frac{2}{3}$,
$4\times\frac{5}{12}=\frac{5}{12}+\frac{5}{12}+\frac{5}{12}+\frac{5}{12}=\frac{20}{12}=(1\frac{8}{12})\ 1\frac{2}{3}$
$4\times\frac{2}{3}=\frac{2}{3}+\frac{2}{3}+\frac{2}{3}+\frac{2}{3}=\frac{8}{3}=2\frac{2}{3}$,
$3\times\frac{5}{6}=\frac{5}{6}+\frac{5}{6}+\frac{5}{6}=\frac{15}{6}=(2\frac{3}{6})\ 2\frac{1}{2}$

Page 66: $\frac{1}{2}$ of $\frac{3}{4}=\frac{3}{8}$, $\frac{1}{3}$ of $\frac{1}{2}=\frac{1}{6}$, $\frac{1}{2}$ of $\frac{5}{6}=$;
$\frac{1}{4}$ of $\frac{8}{12}=\frac{2}{12}$ or $\frac{1}{6}$, $\frac{1}{3}$ of $\frac{9}{10}=\frac{3}{10}$,
$\frac{1}{4}$ of $\frac{4}{6}=\frac{1}{6}$

Page 67: How many $\frac{1}{3}$s can cover 1? 3;
How many $\frac{1}{8}$s can cover $\frac{1}{2}$? 4;
How many $\frac{1}{6}$s can cover $\frac{2}{3}$? 4;
How many $\frac{1}{12}$s can cover $\frac{5}{6}$? 10;
How many $\frac{2}{5}$s can cover $\frac{8}{10}$? 2

Page 68: How many $\frac{1}{4}$s can cover $\frac{1}{2}$? 2;
How many $\frac{1}{3}$s can cover $\frac{1}{2}$? $1\frac{1}{2}$;
How many $\frac{3}{4}$s can cover $\frac{1}{2}$? $\frac{2}{3}$;
How many $\frac{3}{4}$s can cover 1? $1\frac{1}{3}$;
How many $\frac{1}{2}$s can cover $\frac{5}{10}$? 1

Page 69: $\frac{1}{2}=\frac{50}{100}=0.50$ or 0.5, $\frac{1}{4}=\frac{25}{100}=0.25$,
column 1: $\frac{1}{8}=\frac{12.5}{100}=0.125$,
column 2: $\frac{1}{5}=\frac{20}{100}=0.20$ or 0.2, $\frac{1}{10}=\frac{10}{100}=0.10$ or
0.1, $1=\frac{100}{100}=1.00$ or 1,
column 3: $\frac{1}{3}\approx\frac{33}{100}=0.33$, $\frac{1}{6}\approx\frac{17}{100}=0.17$,
$\frac{1}{12}\approx\frac{8}{100}=0.08$

Page 70: $\frac{1}{2}=\frac{50}{100}=50\%$, $\frac{1}{4}=\frac{25}{100}=25\%$,
column 1: $\frac{1}{8}=\frac{12.5}{100}=12.5\%$,
column 2: $\frac{1}{5}=\frac{20}{100}=20\%$, $\frac{1}{10}=\frac{10}{100}=10\%$,
$1=\frac{100}{100}=100\%$,
column 3: $\frac{1}{3}\approx\frac{33}{100}=33\%$, $\frac{1}{6}\approx\frac{17}{100}=17\%$, $\frac{1}{12}\approx\frac{8}{100}=8\%$

Page 78: $\frac{6}{8}=\frac{3}{4}$, $\frac{5}{10}=\frac{1}{2}$, $\frac{4}{6}=\frac{2}{3}$, $\frac{8}{10}=\frac{4}{5}$, $\frac{9}{12}=\frac{3}{4}$

Solutions

Page 79: row 1: $\frac{1}{2}<\frac{4}{6}$, $\frac{3}{8}>\frac{1}{4}$, $\frac{3}{5}<\frac{3}{4}$, $\frac{5}{6}>\frac{5}{10}$; row 2: $\frac{2}{3}=\frac{8}{12}$, $\frac{2}{3}<\frac{3}{4}$, $\frac{5}{8}<\frac{5}{6}$, $\frac{4}{6}=\frac{8}{12}$

Page 80: top: $\frac{7}{4}=1\frac{3}{4}$, $\frac{25}{8}=3\frac{1}{8}$, $\frac{14}{3}=4\frac{2}{3}$; bottom: $\frac{10}{4}=2\frac{2}{4}=2\frac{1}{2}$, $\frac{20}{6}=3\frac{2}{6}=3\frac{1}{3}$, $\frac{14}{4}=3\frac{2}{4}=3\frac{1}{2}$

Page 81: top: $\frac{2}{3}=\frac{8}{12}$, $\frac{3}{4}=\frac{9}{12}$; bottom: $\frac{1}{4}=\frac{2}{8}$ and $\frac{3}{8}=\frac{3}{8}$, $\frac{1}{3}=\frac{4}{12}$ and $\frac{1}{4}=\frac{3}{12}$, $\frac{2}{5}=\frac{4}{10}$ and $\frac{1}{2}=\frac{5}{10}$, $\frac{3}{4}=\frac{9}{12}$ and $\frac{5}{6}=\frac{10}{12}$

Page 83: row 1: $\frac{4}{8}+\frac{3}{8}=\frac{7}{8}$, $\frac{5}{12}+\frac{4}{12}=\frac{9}{12}=\frac{3}{4}$, $\frac{7}{10}+\frac{6}{10}=\frac{13}{10}=1\frac{3}{10}$; row 2: $\frac{8}{10}+\frac{5}{10}=\frac{13}{10}=1\frac{3}{10}$, $\frac{8}{12}+\frac{3}{12}=\frac{11}{12}$, $\frac{10}{12}+\frac{9}{12}=\frac{19}{12}=1\frac{7}{12}$; row 3: $\frac{9}{10}+\frac{5}{10}=\frac{14}{10}=1\frac{4}{10}=1\frac{2}{5}$, $\frac{5}{6}+\frac{4}{6}=\frac{9}{6}=1\frac{3}{6}=1\frac{1}{2}$, $\frac{5}{12}+\frac{9}{12}=\frac{14}{12}=1\frac{2}{12}=1\frac{1}{6}$

Page 85: row 1: $\frac{7}{8}-\frac{4}{8}=\frac{3}{8}$, $\frac{8}{12}-\frac{5}{12}=\frac{3}{12}=\frac{1}{4}$, $\frac{5}{10}-\frac{3}{10}=\frac{2}{10}=\frac{1}{5}$; row 2: $1\frac{8}{12}-\frac{3}{12}=1\frac{5}{12}$, $\frac{6}{4}-\frac{3}{4}=\frac{3}{4}$, $\frac{9}{12}-\frac{5}{12}=\frac{4}{12}=\frac{1}{3}$; row 3: $\frac{11}{10}-\frac{6}{10}=\frac{5}{10}=\frac{1}{2}$, $\frac{10}{12}-\frac{9}{12}=\frac{1}{12}$, $\frac{13}{8}-\frac{6}{8}=\frac{7}{8}$

Page 87: row 1: $1\frac{1}{3}$, $2\frac{1}{4}$, $\frac{3}{4}$; row 2: $1\frac{1}{2}$, $2\frac{1}{2}$, $1\frac{1}{5}$; row 3: $\frac{1}{4}$, $\frac{3}{8}$, $\frac{1}{10}$; row 4: $\frac{1}{2}$, $\frac{3}{8}$, $\frac{2}{5}$

Page 89: 2, 2; 4, 4; 4, 4; 4, 4; 3, 3; 2, 2; $\frac{1}{2}$, $\frac{1}{2}$

Page 90: For $\frac{1}{8}$s, $\frac{1}{10}$s, and $\frac{1}{12}$s, use the appropriate fraction tiles to make the marks on the number line. For $\frac{1}{9}$s, use $\frac{1}{3}$ of the $\frac{1}{3}$ tile to make the marks on the number line.

Page 91: Make the ruler and measure objects in the classroom (refer to Teaching Notes).

Fraction Materials

Fraction Circle Materials
LER 617 *Deluxe Rainbow Fraction Circles*
LER 115 *Basic Rainbow Fraction Circles*
LER 618 *Overhead Deluxe Rainbow Fraction Circles*
LER 315 *Overhead Basic Fraction Circles*

Fraction Square Materials
LER 620 *Deluxe Rainbow Fraction Squares*
LER 116 *Basic Rainbow Fraction Squares*
LER 620 *Overhead Deluxe Rainbow Fraction Squares*
LER 251 *Overhead Basic Rainbow Fraction Squares*

Fraction Flashcards
LER 622 *Fraction Circle Flashcards*
LER 623 *Fraction Square & Decimal Flashcards*

Rainbow Fraction Tile Materials
LER 615 *Rainbow Fraction Tiles*
LER 616 *Overhead Rainbow Fraction Tiles*

Wonderful Work
★☆ Certificate ★☆

To: _____

For: _____
_____

Date _____   **Teacher** _____

★★★★★★★★★★★★★★★★

Fractions Are Easy
★★☆ Award ★★☆

To: _____

For: _____
_____

Date _____   **Teacher** _____

★★★★★★★★★★★★★★★★